PRAISE FOR T[

"Whether it is a physical ailment or crisis of spirit, Colin goes deep at a sacred and special level. A compassionate doctor for your heart, brain, soul, and all your other fantastic body parts, Dr. Colin Zhu will inspire the THRIVE in you!"

— *Angie Krause, Global Leadership Consultant and Business Intuitive*

"Colin's enthusiasm, kindness, insightfulness, and openness make *Thrive Medicine* shine. His advice will help the reader grow and permit true healthfulness with intention. This young man has and shares heartfelt wisdom. Dr. Zhu walks the walk. I think we should all walk it with him."

— *Dan Wilensky, MD, Family Physician, former travel doctor and solo traveler, vegan, and middle-of-the-pack triathlete*

"A powerful book that will take you on a journey to explore your core and purpose, elevating your mind beyond every day to inquire into the deeper meaning we all crave. This is a healing guide within Colin's personal narrative and is driven by a genuine passion to share the foundation for living a life full of abundance."

— *Ingrid Edshteyn, DO, Founder of Valia Lifestyle*

"In a new and different age, an age of greater enlightenment, awareness, health — both personal and societal — our healers, our doctors, will be shining lights to guide us. They will walk the walk as well as talk the talk. They will have wide comprehensive visions. They will understand how health starts with behavior, lifestyle, and diet. They will teach us through their example how to defeat illness and disease by not allowing it to even take root and instead how to thrive in a healthy balanced life fully lived. We must already be at that age because Dr. Colin Zhu exists and has written this book on these principles of a new medicine."

— *Richard LaMarita, Chef, Natural Gourmet Institute*

THRIVE
MEDICINE

How to Cultivate Your Desires
and Elevate Your Life

COLIN ZHU, DO

Thrive Medicine:
How to Cultivate Your Desires and Elevate Your Life

Copyright © 2017 by Colin Zhu, DO

To contact the author, visit
www.chefdoczhu.com
Instagram @thechefdoc

Print ISBN-13: 978-0-9996461-3-7
Ebook ISBN-13: 978-0-9996461-2-0

Also available in Spanish print and e-book versions
and English audiobook format

Printed in the United States of America

Cover design: Alan Dino Hebel, Ian Koviak
Interior design: Carla Green
Inside author picture: Kat Lazo
Cover author picture: Christopher Cheng

With love and gratitude to all my family members, friends, teachers, mentors, and all those who I hold dear, who have supported me till this day and continue to do so. I could not have done this without any of you.

You are my world.

To all those who want more out of life: attack it with hunger, humor, grace and, most importantly, a little fun.

Contents

The Components of Thrive Medicine

Preface

I was born to two immigrant Chinese parents that came from another culture, society, and generation. Essentially from another world. With that in mind, they brought with them certain belief systems and life experiences. Like most Chinese parents, they wanted security for their children in regard to finances, jobs and careers, and certain life partners. There is nothing is wrong with that. However, there was something missing from this standard formula. It was lacking exploration, romance, wonder, and passion. Therefore, I chose to create my own formula, my own story.

» I became a doctor to care and to teach.

» I became a chef to nourish curious minds.

» I competed in triathlons to push mental and physical boundaries.

» I traveled the world to learn more about humanity.

» I wrote this book to share my story, so you can create yours.

What I offer here, simply put, is a collection of reflections, experiences, and perspectives of my journey through life. Personally, I have not only braved through the challenging, often treacherous, waters of the medical world, but I've also dabbled in some beautiful culinary landscapes. I've participated in triathlons, racing across land and sea to meet the proverbial finish line and, finally, I have had the opportunity to venture to over thirty countries across seven continents. I have studied with several mentors, authors, speakers, and coaches. I have personally coached my own clients, seen thousands of patients, and have been a patient myself. I have been through the highest of highs as well as through depression, heartbreak, and death.

This book represents a full expression of myself, and is solely dedicated to those in life's shackles to let you know that there is always another way to live once you decide to make a different choice. However, how you decide to use it is entirely up to you. This is your life and YOU, my friend, are the driver. Only you have the power to change everything that is right in front of you. You have an effect on everyone around you, both positively and negatively and, if I may, I implore you to use this book while considering your own innate intuition a.k.a. your gut feelings. Use it in the context of your own unique life and use it with both love and respect for yourself, along with all life-forms around you. So, are you ready?

My mission in life is not merely to survive, but to thrive; and to do so with some passion, some compassion, some humor, and some style.
— Maya Angelou

Introduction:
To Thrive or Not?

This book, my friends, is your compass that guides you to whatever it is that you want in life. There are no rules to this. This can help provide guidance on finding a better career, navigating better relationships, or perhaps simply encouraging you on how to embrace all of the ups and downs of life. However, this isn't exactly an end-all-be-all life instruction manual or a step-by-step guide. The idea of this book is to provide some direction to help you not just live your life, but to thrive.

So, you might ask, "What exactly does it mean to thrive?" According to Webster's Dictionary, "thrive" means to flourish or to succeed or to prosper. When I founded *TheChefDoc*, an online wellness and lifestyle brand platform in January of 2017, I chose three main ingredients to living your best life.

1. **Culinary Medicine** or essentially, food as medicine.

2. **Lifestyle Medicine**[1] or using evidence based lifestyle approaches to prevent, treat and reverse chronic lifestyle related diseases.

3. **Thrive Medicine**

WHAT IS THRIVE MEDICINE?

Thrive medicine is the specific driving force for a person to seek a deeper, higher quality understanding of themselves and more enjoyment out of their lives. It allows you to be in a more positive mindset to arrive to your sole (and soul) purpose. It allows space to explore free will, choice, and individual thought patterns.

In other words, thrive medicine is the energy, drive, gusto needed to arrive at your uninhibited passions.

The Okinawans call this "Ikigai." The Nicoyans of Costa Rica call it "plan de vida." I call this your reason for being. People can have the healthiest diets or live the grandest lifestyle, but without thrive medicine, it is more challenging to find enjoyment, satisfaction and, ultimately, awareness out of your life's purpose.

This book is set up in a way that each chapter can function independently. Feel free to read it in any order. Read the chapters that call to and resonate with you. After you read a chapter, apply the actions it recommends. You may find that when you reread a chapter at a later time, you may think that the book has changed. In reality, it is *YOU* who has changed.

The empty notes at the end of each chapter are meant for you to jot down your immediate thoughts and actions. Your first gut reaction is usually the correct one. These notes are designed to cultivate a newer you, a new blueprint. My hope is that you take away anything you can use and apply to your own life, however small it may be.

Without change and progress, we cannot grow as human beings. Welcome *change*, do not *resist* it. This is your guide to a better version of yourself. This book is about pushing and digging deep with the intention of expanding the boundaries of who you are and what you *think* you can do.

Chapter 1

Life

"We are not made to survive. We are not made to manage our pain or get through it. We are made to be creators of our lives. We can create anything. Anything we can dream about, we can create it."

— Tony Robbins

In the grand scheme of your life, is it more important to live fully and deeply or just simply longer? In the U.S., the average life expectancy of an individual is 78.8 years according to 2014 CDC data[2]. Despite this, we do not essentially know how long we are meant to be here. We are not guaranteed any amount of time, or anything for that matter. You could be here for the next fifty years or, God forbid, until tomorrow.

There is a great music video by the band Nickelback called *Savin' Me*. In this video, the character is saved by a stranger from getting run over by a bus. Suddenly, he is surrounded by the sight of expiring timestamps above everyone's head. Not only is he perplexed and confused, but he is able to see the finite nature of our mortality. Now, for example, if we were able to see the timestamps above our heads, how would you act differently?

Would you choose to live your life more recklessly? Or would you live your life more thoughtfully and consciously?

It all comes down to the freedom of choice.

From cave drawings dating back to the prehistoric era to the Age of Reason of the Renaissance to modern day think-tanks, we have evolved amazingly as human beings. We have been able to reach a point where we have more free thought and free will than we have ever had. With that gift, we have the power of *choice*; the power to choose the path which you want your life to take. Whether you realize it or not, you are the *driver* of your own life and you have a myriad of paths to travel. The question is: *which way do I go?* There is no wrong answer to this. You have full control over how you want to approach it.

Another way to look at this is to ask yourself this: *Are you living the day-to-day routine?* For instance: A person wakes up, goes to school and/or goes to work, grows up, makes money, raises a family, retires, and dies. This is what I like to call the *default life.* Does this sound like you? Now, don't get me wrong. I am not knocking the *default life.* If you are totally satisfied with this, then close this book now and move on with your beautiful life. I am speaking to those who want a change or who know that there is *something deeper inside of them that yearns for something more*—something that an award, a paycheck, a degree, or a title cannot give them. Something that wakes them up in the middle of the night because they know that they cannot continue to live the way that they have been living. Something buried inside them that yells out that they are meant for something bigger than themselves. Something that is willing to serve and give back to humanity in some way. Something that makes them feel they are more connected to the whole when, in fact, we are, and we have never been alone. Let me pose these questions:

If I die tomorrow, will I have regrets?

Have I so far lived out my life in earnest?

Have I been truthful, honest, and authentic with myself?

Have I fully expressed myself each day and in every way possible?

Have I accomplished what my heart has desired?

The answers to these questions will help determine whether you are ready to take your life to the next chapter, but more notably the next level. However, before we address that, let us explore what your blocks are, what prevent you from reaching this pivotal step. Blocks prevent us from living our best life.

As a nation in 2016, we have faced many challenging events: mass shootings, missing airplanes, questionable elections, gender issues, and race debates. We have a choice. We can either choose to buy into the negativity around us OR be the *light* that shines upon others. *Why don't we cut out the noise instead?* The noise that I am referring to is the arguments and debates about the different facets of what make us human, such as our appearances, belief systems, religions, political perspectives, etc. These facets make us very colorful, but they can also distract us from the basic essence of being human. The basic essence of being human is the fact that we are interconnected with all lifeforms on this planet and we have the great potential to create. Let us focus instead on the gifts of being human. Let us consider the art, music, and dance—essentially our undeniable creativity.

The sacredness of life is that it can end at a moment's notice, and before you have the chance to catch up and realize what has happened, it may be too late. *So, cut out the noise!* It is very easy to get caught up in someone else's opinion or how society wants you to be. No doubt, we live in a vast and sophisticated world, and it can be very tempting to want to compare ourselves to another. We are easily influenced by our neighbors, so to speak. Cutting out the noise means not letting the voices outside of you drive your decisions, and not letting others determine who you are. Standing on your own as an individual means removing the blocks to your own greatness.

Once you determine who you are and who you need to be in your life, then the next question to ask is: *where do your priorities lay?* Do you wake up because you have to make it to work in the morning, fight the morning commute, finish a deadline, make money to put food on the table, pay bills and pay rent?

What is it that motivates you to wake up?

If you are like the millions of others who are unaware of why they get up or have not consciously thought about this question, then you are just merely surviving or just getting by. The point of this question is to force you to focus on your TOP priorities, wishes, regrets, and desires, and bring them to the forefront.

Priorities allow us to set what comes first, but what is it that comes first for you? I am not referring to your family obligations or your work duties. These are necessary for the practical portions of your life, but I am referring to something else. I am talking about the hidden desires of your being. When was the last time you asked yourself what it is that you truly want? What is it that you yearn for?

Let's try some brief exercises *(these will be expanded upon in later chapters)*:

» *Have a focus and a vision.* Without an actual direction in life, how do you know where you are going? If you do not know, then you are just *spinning your wheels.* Without a map or a compass, we are constantly lost and wandering, unless you are satisfied with staying in place. Having a focus and vision help you set your sights on something that pulls you forward. Having a target pushes you to concentrate your energies and your essence toward something bigger than yourself. Have you ever driven towards your own greatness and potential before? Your greatness is defined as having a positive impact on another human being. Remember that we are all interconnected. For example, helping to build a home for Habitat for Humanity for those affected by a natural disaster, helping to cook at a food shelter, giving a small business loan to an entrepreneur and watching it take off, or simply holding an elderly person's hand to cross the street. Your greatness does not have to result in superhero feats all the time. It simply means to imprint on another to do good. It simply means to inspire.

» *Ask what is missing from your life?* When you take a step back and look at the big picture, we are addicted to many things: smartphone, computer, social media, television, fast food, alcohol, marijuana and other recreational street drugs. What they all share is the fact that they all give you a certain limited high which is soon followed by a certain low. Another way to look at this is that you become a slave to those external substances. In the end, we turn to these things because we seek to fill up a certain void in our lives. What is that for you? Could it be peace, love, drive, passion, or purpose?

» *Find your own voice.* We have this inner voice that talks to us all the time. "I am 'this or that'," or, "I am not good enough for this part," or, "I can't do this because I am not talented." Your inner voice or, as I like to call it, your chatterbox, can dictate what you *should* do, how you *should* do it, and when you *should* do it. Our chatterbox is an accumulation of voices from our parents, friends, teachers, and society. These all have had a profound effect on us and have influenced us in more ways than one. Finding our own voice is honing in on our own intuition or gut feelings. This is more representative of our *truth*. Listening to our gut will lead us to better choices instead of the outside voices that we encounter on a daily basis.

» *Go mad. Go crazy.* There is something very mundane about the default life. Not so much boring, but predictable. Isn't it maddening to follow a crowd in the same direction, or worse, follow a crowd and NOT know where you are going? Robert Frost tells us to take the road less traveled and that it will make all the difference. To go mad means to have a thirst or hunger for something entirely different for yourself. Go outside your comfort zone and create an alternative reality for yourself. Perhaps choose an offbeat route to work, venture on an uncommon vacation alone, savor a different cuisine, or take up a new hobby.

» ***Change the way you think.*** How we fair through life depends in many ways on our outlook, specifically with regard to our attitude and perception. The world does not revolve around you. *We simply live in the world.* As events and people cross our path, we have the greatest gift of choosing how we react to them. Contrary to what you may think, *we actually do not have control over anything.* Please reread that last statement. Take a moment to process that. This is a powerful shift if it can be implemented correctly. For example, emotions may rise from a heated debate with your best friend. Instead of being overwhelmed by your emotions, you can lessen your perception of control, thereby holding fewer grudges in the future. Another way of not succumbing to your emotions is to just observe how things really are and to not judge them. Just observe the emotions and do not react to them. We will explore this further in other chapters.

» ***Be present.*** How often do you practice being in the here and now? What I mean by this is to be completely devoid of distractions and mindless chatter in our heads, and to be fully immersed in this present moment. Why is this important? *Well, it is the only thing that matters.* The past is history and the future is not guaranteed, yet we spend the majority of our time "living" in either one of the two. We think about what is to come, such as birthdays, deadlines, weddings, the weekend, but we do not live in the present moment. We reminisce and relish on our past and our memories, but we do not live in the "now" as it passes us by. *Be right here.*

» ***Our time is extremely precious.*** Ever wonder how some people are able to accomplish so much within a short period of time? Some people are able to create their own companies within 2-3 years, and others are able to train for racing competitions rather quickly. Some are able to reach deadlines quickly, while some still reach their destinations sooner. Even though this is not a race, the point is that we all have the same exact amount of time. We all have 24 hours in a day. We just have to choose how to effectively manage it. Time is a limited commodity and it is non-replenishable. Once you spend it, you can no longer get it back. This goes for the time you spend with loved ones, your work and career, passions, and personal time. Time is more precious than any tangible object. So, the question is: where would you like to devote and invest your time?

» ***Practice gratitude and humility.*** This is an awesome habit to have. To be able to give thanks and practice modesty enhances your overall character. To acknowledge that achievements are the result of our collective helps embrace unity, fellowship, and brotherhood. This can be done right now. Practice gratitude for the things, events, and people in your life, whether those things have left behind a positive or negative impact on your life. How you choose to have a particular experience affect you is entirely up to you. Humility enhances selflessness.

"Mastery is choosing to use the situations we find ourselves in rather than letting them use us. All you need to do to radically change your life is to make the choice to see your triumphs and your tragedies as invitations to grow and evolve."
-DEBBIE FORD

The purpose of the aforementioned exercises are to help you rethink how you have been living your life. Create a different perspective than previously thought. The following chapters will continue to expand on these concepts.

Everything that you see before you, from the tallest skyscrapers to nanocomputer chips to trips to Mars, all came from a single thought. Man has accomplished ungodly things and feats. These all came from an idea, an inspiration, or a dream. I am not urging you to invent the next big thing, per say, but what I am encouraging you to do is to go beyond what you think or believe is possible.

Nothing is impossible.

When you choose to believe that something is impossible or unachievable, what you are actually doing is creating a block for yourself. A limiting belief. And when you have enough of these, you will create a total gridlock on your life. Have you ever met that grumpy elderly man that is cynical about everything?

There is no limit to what you can do in this world. If you want to sing in your own concert, YOU can. If you desire to be CEO of your own company, YOU can be. If you want the most loving relationship, YOU can have it. If you want to have the best life possible, guess what? YOU can. It all falls upon you. Make it the greatest!

ACTION STEPS

- Make a list of your true desires in life. At the bare minimum, what is the ONE thing you want to do/achieve? How will you go about doing this? Write down the steps.

- Make a list of what prevents you from reaching your desires.

- Make a list of steps to eradicate roadblocks or limiting beliefs.

Your thoughts. Your roadmap. Your next steps...

Chapter 2

Doing

*"Productivity is driven by
purpose and priority."*
— GARY KELLER, CO-AUTHOR, *THE ONE THING*

Picture how a plate juggler is able to balance three or four spinning plates at a time? Amazing act, right? Well, unless you are a seasoned plate juggler, I would not suggest applying that same principle to your own life. It is vital to recognize that you have limits and boundaries. Not to say that everything on your to-do list is not important, but there are things that must take priority. As a society, we love to be busy, but sometimes that does not equate to being productive.

> I took up triathlon racing since my last year in college and have been hooked ever since. My car was finally loaded for the weekend with my tri-bike firmly hung on the back rack. Shoes and the rest of my racing gear were in. *Hmm...something is missing*, I thought to myself. *Oh, yes, my helmet.* I turned around to make my way towards the apartment.
>
> "Is this what you were looking for?" Maddy asked, giving me a cheeky grin.

I laughed in response. My friend decided to tag along with me to my New Hampshire triathlon. I was two states away from completing my New England tour of races. Connecticut, check. Massachusetts, check. Rhode Island, check. Vermont, check. This is all part of my insane desire to race in every state of the United States of America. After a long week of hospital call, I was ready to get away. Some might call me a weekend warrior, but I took it to a whole different level. I had scheduled two races back to back with minimum time to train due to my extensive hours working on the hospital floors. Then, on top of that, my family had planned to visit me after all the races were finished. *Did I mention I have this unhealthy habit of spreading myself too thin?* I always have this notion that there just isn't enough time in a day. So, I had to jam everything in.

Thirty minutes after packing, we were on the road, heading north. Clear skies and open highways welcomed us. It was perfect 73-degree weather. Windows were down. The radio was playing *Jon Bon Jovi* and we were cruising all the way up. We had just finished up a conversation about the ridiculous number of cat videos on YouTube when Maddy decided to take a nap. I continued to drive us down route I-93 when, out of the corner of my eye, a deer crossed over the opposite lanes, the median, and then into my lane.

All sounds ceased at that moment. My heart thumped out of my chest.

My gut reaction took over all my senses, and instead of hitting the brakes, I slammed on the accelerator. Milliseconds flew by as I drove right through the poor animal and swerved into the right shoulder lane. I quickly pulled over and stopped the car. Maddy looked at me with shock and disbelief. My immediate reaction was to be thankful that we were both alive, however, my heart ached for the death of that poor deer.

Fast forward to the present.

This had been a life-changing perspective on my view on "being busy" just for the sake of being busy. Looking back, I reflected on what had led up to that day. *Why did this incident happen?* Skies and driving conditions were clear. I was not sleepy or drunk. I did not text or call while driving. Sure, you can say that this was just a coincidence and deer run out all the time. For me, I came to a conclusion after consulting a few people. My life, at that point, was in a state of disarray and chaos that left me unfocused on where my direction was going. Between work, family and personal obligations, I had spread myself too thin. It was analogous to grabbing sand and trying to hold onto every single grain. Things will eventually fall apart, just like this highway incident. In case you were curious, I did, indeed, cancel the subsequent two races after that day. In the end, I was not mindful of what I was doing.

This was one of the most challenging phases of my life because I was in the middle of my medical residency. For others, it may be maintaining a mortgage, shuttling children to football practice, keeping your restaurant business intact, or simply keeping promises you thought you could keep. For myself, having to juggle eighty-hour work weeks (at times, more), paying bills and student loans, and maintaining personal relationships and family obligations presented to be such a balancing act that sometimes it resulted in calamity, as highlighted in my deer incident. This was a result of *mindlessness.*

Coming back to the concept of "being busy" in our society, let's face it, we live in a "no pain, no gain" world. Consequently, we love to be busy and are obsessed with putting a lot on our plates. We have adapted to doing more and more and have pushed ourselves to the maximum. You cannot do everything and expect to feel satisfied and content because there is a limit to what you can do *at any moment in time.* I am a firm believer that humans are capable of anything, but we tend to do things in a mindless fashion without fully comprehending what we are doing, or at least what we are paying attention to at the present moment. *So, what is the alternative approach to this?* Being mindful of your daily tasks is one approach.

Let's first explore some research on overworking.

Take, for example, long overtime work hours. Jack Nevison, a business and computing consultant, gathered many scientific papers[3] to highlight that more hours do not necessarily mean more productivity.

In addition, according to the CDC, long overtime hours have been associated with poor general health perception, increased injury rates and illness, weight gain, alcohol consumption, smoking, and even death[4]. So, as you can see, it is not just a matter of getting things done for the sake of completion. Your "overworking" leads to negative health effects.

What is the purpose of *overworking* then? When your work has a clear direction and focus, strategies can be implemented to improve efficacy and efficiency, thus less strain on you. As a physician, I can tell you firsthand that stress has emotional, mental, and physical health effects. This applied to me as well because this has not always been the case with me. There was a time in my life where I was not able to focus on the present or the moments in front of me. Let's ask a few questions about why we overwork ourselves:

Why are we obsessed with *doing* so much?

Why are some of us in this perpetual *rat race*?

After we achieve "X" number of things, do we actually feel satisfied?

Sometimes it may be challenging to answer these questions because "being busy" and overworking has been, for some of us, a lifestyle that we have adapted to and something we rarely question.

What do I recommend? Well, it starts with me asking the patient, "What is the goal of you doing so much? What is it that you are trying to accomplish?"

Let's strategize:

So, if one approach is to be mindful and focused on your work, you may be thinking that this is easier said than done. And you would be right. However, like most things in life, focusing and being present takes practice and a keen sense of awareness.

The first step is to be mindful, and the second is to prioritize:

> **What needs to be done first or as soon as possible?**
>
> **Who do I have to answer to first?**
>
> **Is this issue something urgent or can it wait?**

Next time you encounter a "juggling situation," ask the previous questions. You, in turn, take out tasks that can be accomplished later and not right now. You take less important things off of your priority plate. By doing this, you minimize the burden on yourself. How do you know if you are doing this correctly? Excellent question. Well, you will feel *lighter* first of all. The less you put on yourself, the less stress you will have. The less stress you have, the MORE focus and energy you will have for the other things that need attention. The point is to do less or to *consolidate*. And when at all possible, *DELEGATE*! It is completely okay to ask for help. You are only one person. You can only do so much until that "check engine light" comes on and you are near the breaking point.

One of my favorite analogies is that of the security checkpoint prior to takeoff on a flight. If you have ever had the opportunity to fly on an airplane, this is one of the many procedural steps flight staff take to ensure safety. In the event of an emergency during a flight, oxygen masks drop down from the ceiling and oxygen starts to flow. For those who have been on a plane before, who do they say to place the mask on first? You or the person next to you? (Hint: look in a mirror.)

> **That's right, YOU!**

I constantly apply this analogy to my patients' wellbeing. If you do not take care and set yourself as a priority first, you cannot take on this world with style and finesse. Some of you who are reading this are mothers, bosses, priests, caretakers, community leaders, managers—people depend and rely on you. You've decided to serve others through your sense of duty and passion. What would it be like if you did not take care of yourself? Here is how taking on too much will play out:

> **[Stress (from obligation, fear, or guilt) → lack of sleep, loss of appetite, weight changes, poor relationships, etc. → sickness → chronic disease (in the form of hypertension, diabetes, thyroid imbalance, cancer, etc. as a result of not seeing a health care provider earlier because you can "stick or ride it out.") → Death]**

Get the picture? Let's continue.

Learn to say, "No."

There are some people we like to call "people pleasers." I have no doubt that if you take a few moments, you will be able to think of a couple of people exactly like that. What do these people have in common? They choose not to say no for fear of displeasing another. Some consider this a weakness or a "bad" attribute. Over time, these people disempower themselves because they choose to make others a priority instead of themselves. So, how do people pleasers differ from, for example, people who are actual caregivers? It comes down to choices. Caregivers made the choice to care for another person, whether it is in a professional capacity or not. A people pleaser relinquishes their freedom of choice to that other person, thereby disempowering themselves.

So, what does learning to *say, "No,"* do?

Saying, "No," creates a proverbial boundary between you and the other person who is asking something from you that they cannot do at that moment. Saying, "No," also fosters self-respect. By saying no, you choose to respect your own time and energy by not letting it leak elsewhere where it may not serve any benefit. Lastly, it prevents you from adding more to your *already full plate.* Only you are aware of how much you can give or take at any given time. We are all unique individuals and have different capacities of what we can handle.

> **It is okay to say no. Let me say this again.**
> **It is OKAY to say no.**

The world will *not* shatter into pieces. It will *not* end. Worst case scenario? The person asking... will ask someone else. Done. Move on.

» **Prioritize.** Let's reiterate this here. Take a look at what you *need* to do versus what you *want* to do. The things you NEED to do come first. What are those? Well, it depends on what you prioritize. Utility bills and mortgages. Family obligations. Work projects that are due. Your spouse's needs. Your children's needs. What are your wants? Is buying that fancy grill for the barbecue or that fifth Michael Kors bag necessary? What would come first then? Your daughter's piano recital or a Sunday night football game with your friends? When you make a to-do list, prioritize what is most important or urgent and accomplish those first. It is okay if you choose to prioritize your others' needs and desires before yourself. There is nothing wrong with that, but remember to also address your own wants and desires as well. This will allow more balance, satisfaction, and contentment in your life.

» **Let go.** Attachments to events, things, and people cause humans a lot of unnecessary suffering. In the proverbial rat race, things such as money, status, and degrees tend to dominate our concern and attention. There is always a perception that these things make the "world go around." Entertain this common hypothetical scenario: If we let go of our attachments to things, including money, then what should we be motivated by then? What makes your priorities important? Let go of attachments that take you away from accomplishing your *real* priorities.

» *Simplify*. Declutter the unnecessary things in your life. This can be applied to people, actual things, or anything that takes time, focus, and energy away from your daily activities. Get rid of anything that sucks your time and causes mental strain. Things that cause mental strain are things that do not contribute to your overall goal or set of priorities. For example, taking an extra shift for a friend when you could be working your guitar audition. Another might be hanging out with coworkers instead of devoting more time to your psychology thesis. Also consider consolidating your list. If certain things can be accomplished in one step instead of five, then do it. Why exert extra energy?

> **Remember to ask: how is what I am doing significant to my overall *life*?**
>
> **Are there items I can remove from my "heavy spinning plates"?**

In our practical life, we have bills to pay, family obligations, and work duties. By simplifying your life, you leave room for the important things, and thus get the most out of them. Make sure you separate your practical life from your own inner desires and the steps you need to accomplish them. When you accomplish your inner desires, this represents how brilliant you are. You get to share who you are and not just add to the "mindless doing." What you do is great work, and your work affects everyone around you and afar, whether you realize it or not.

ACTION STEPS

- Take some time out and *do* absolutely nothing! This will take practice and patience.

- Take a technology, phone, and social media *fast* for one day, one week, or one month. Write down how you felt during this at every stage.

- Consolidating or minimizing your *to-do* list will also destress you. Simplicity is key!

- Make two columns and label them: Practical-human life vs. Impacting-the-world life. Then list out the steps needed to accomplish both.

Your thoughts. Your roadmap. Your next steps...

Chapter 3

Wanderlust

*"The real voyage of discovery consists
not in seeking new landscapes,
but in having new eyes."*
— Marcel Proust

There is no comparison to traveling on your own. It all started at a young age for me. I was fortunate to have been able to travel with my family growing up. Although it started out with road trips to Disneyland from our New Jersey home every summer, it later progressed to European tours and visits to the Great Wall in China. My family had already planted that seed of exploration and curiosity in me that has continued and flourished in my adult years. From my travels, I learned some valuable lessons that I impart onto my patients.

1. *Observe and listen.* These two skills plus compassion are, in my opinion, the three greatest tools to have as a physician. Here is an excerpt from my trip to Queensland, Australia highlighting this:

> Something has shifted yet again. I feel rejuvenated. I gave a deep exhale as I briefly closed my eyes. I tilted my head up as I gazed up at the towering skyscrapers

in the Central Business District of downtown Sydney, Australia. Droves of pedestrians walked passed me as I stood there in the middle of the sidewalk. I felt, despite being surrounded by herds of people, like I was standing alone, immersed in my environment.

What has returned to me again is the feeling of *wonder* and *discovery*. As I strolled south on Pitt Street, I reflected on the previous few days and smiled. I had finally reached my dream of scuba diving in Australia and uncovered a whole new landscape on a new continent— one that had been outside my reach for many years. In the past few days, I have trekked through a tropical rainforest, went scuba diving in the breathtaking Great Barrier Reef, climbed to the top of Sydney Harbour Bridge, and even took up surfing lessons at the famous Bondi Beach.

On the other hand, it is not just the stunning landscapes of the Australian coastlines and beaches or the mesmerizing aerial views of the 2300km length of coral reefs. It is the *people*. I am very impressed by them. Whether it was the young man who gave up his bus seat for an elderly man who came hobbling in with a cane or the sweet female cashier who tried on two t-shirts for me when I was shopping for my younger sister, the Australian people have reminded me that the sense of *community* does permeate through our veins, sometimes instinctively. It has been amazing to witness again.

A sly smirk ran across my face as I chuckled to myself. When you travel, you can run into bumps along the way and, as fate would have it, I did get stung by a jellyfish, almost went into decompression sickness [*where you get aches and pains and can become delirious from too much nitrogen gas in the body from scuba diving... in short, a bad thing*], and, oh yeah, completely forgot about acquiring a travel visa up until the day of my departure to Australia. In some strange fashion, I still made the trip. Like I said, *as fate would have it.*

Observation and listening taught me to utilize my other senses. This is more notable in a completely new environment where you are forced to use them. I constantly train my other senses by traveling. Patients appreciate this even more because I can holistically communicate with them on a deeper level.

2. *Stumbling.* To stumble is to give way, let go of past limiting beliefs, and to recreate yourself, sometimes on a daily basis. Life happens, we run into missteps every day, and that is okay. Just get back on track and learn from them. Sometimes, a dose of innocence is warranted. For me, at the time, it was not doing enough research on acquiring a travel visa before embarking on my trip to Australia. Instead of beating myself up, which I had every opportunity to do, I shrugged it off and moved on. *What was the point of beating myself up? Am I not allowed to be careless at times?* Most of us judge ourselves every day and, sometimes, every moment. It's a *disease.* I had to be gentle with myself, but this is what I love about traveling—the chance to rediscover yourself and to learn over and over again. To me, that was the real point of traveling. The few keen opportunities to learn, grow, mature— in short, wise up. There is no end to it as long as you are willing to open your eyes. If you are an adult reading this, does this mean you are immune to mistakes along the way, that you once made as a child? NO! You are an incredible human being that is always evolving! To *thrive* is to recognize that you are *human.* And a part of being human is allowing yourself to wander, get lost, and stumble. So, take those risks and make those mistakes!

3. *Experiences, not things.* Everyone has their own interests, passions, and hobbies. Mine is travel. There was something magical about traversing to another country, especially a completely new world. Every time I travel, I gain a new set of feelings, sensations, experiences, and lessons that one cannot

get from buying a new car or the latest television set. Having experiences trumps buying materialistic *things*.

"Invest in experiences."

-DAN BUETTNER, NATIONAL GEOGRAPHIC EXPLORER,
AUTHOR OF *THE BLUE ZONES*

Please, do not get me wrong. There is nothing *bad* about acquiring things. It can provide novelty and a certain thrill, but that is only temporary. Acquiring things will give you a false sense of fulfillment and happiness. During my travels to Australia, I was able to strike up a conversation about the educational system with a Norwegian, have a riveting discussion about classical architecture with a German, and ask someone from Russia their opinion of the importance of personal independence. *Where else can you find this?*

Nowhere but out there!!!

4. *Exploration*. Another great aspect of traveling is that it reinforces your personal freedom. A friend of mine once curiously asked me, "How are you able to travel on your own so much? Don't you feel lonely when you travel alone?"

I thought about it for a minute and replied, "It's not so much about if I am able to, it's more about if I am willing to or not." It is not an easy decision if you focus on the reasons NOT to travel. For example, not having the time, money, obligations. However, the ability to be brave and venture on your own brings benefits that are priceless. It's not about what you what you see or do, but what you will experience and take away from your journey, especially the ones that you did not anticipate or plan for.

Trips take a certain amount of planning and organization, but make sure you allow room for spontaneity as well. On the other hand, it also takes a certain amount of courage to go out on your own, especially to a country that you have not been to before or know little about. In beginning, I was hesitant to make that leap to travel solo, but once I did, I never looked back. For all those contemplating traveling on your own soon, please prepare yourself by visiting the popular travel sites and doing your own research. It will go a long way and save you time and resources in the end.

Having time to sightsee can be an obstacle on its own, however. Something interesting to note about the USA is that, compared to other countries, we actually have a lot less opportunity to venture out. According to reports from the Center for Economic Policy and Research (CEPR) in 2013, by law, all the countries in the European Union have at least four work weeks of paid vacation[5]. The USA, on the other hand, does not have a single legally required paid vacation day or holiday[6]. This correlated with my travels to South Africa where I stayed at a local hostel in Cape Town. I met a young girl from Holland and a laborer from Australia. Both reported that it is not uncommon to take a few months off before your next work venture or a new semester for university study. At this point, unless you move out of America, I would not wait until your boss gives you a few days off. *Practice putting money into a "traveling account" and save for a trip of a lifetime.* Or better yet, discover new areas to explore in your own backyard. You do not necessarily need a lavish trip, just one that takes you somewhere new that you have not been to before. Try doing it with a partner or take your family or friends or, like me, just go solo.

> "The man who goes alone can start today,
> but he who travels with another must wait till
> that other is ready."
> —Henry David Thoreau

A few more points…

» ***To travel is to discover yourself.*** In 1983, Howard Schultz traveled to Italy and discovered a romantic Italian coffee culture. He brought the concept back to America and cultivated and enhanced *Starbucks* to what it is today. At the age of forty, Dietrich Mateschitz traveled to Thailand and discovered a jet-lag cure that came in a syrupy-tonic drink. After buying the rights to the small company, he co-founded *Red Bull*. However, you do not need to venture too far like these two gentlemen to find some time with yourself. A stroll through your neighborhood park, beach, or city square works just as well! Put on some jamming music and drown out the outside noise. When you have the opportunity to get away from your routine environment, you have the chance to be able to liberate your mind and soul. When that happens, you will be able to express yourself in ways you may not have had the chance to before. Just think about it: when you are alone, you minimize the number of distractions, interruptions, and interferences. So, the fewer distractions you have, the clearer you can be with yourself.

» *To travel is to listen and understand others.* The opportunity to be able to communicate with another person from a different world is priceless. It goes beyond reading about it in a book or watching it on the Travel Channel or in the movies. You will have the opportunity to see someone else's world through their eyes. For instance, the people of India treat cows as sacred beings. They view the animal as a symbol of the earth and as a nourisher. The love of soccer starts at a very young age in Brazil. Sometimes they learn to kick a soccer ball before they can walk. In South Africa, it is not uncommon when you greet a person, instead of the typical "good," or, "I'm fine" responses, they respond by saying, "Hundreds!" Learning another's customs or culture provides you with insight and, with that, increased respect and tolerance. We are more similar than different despite what we may look like on the outside.

» *To travel is to uncover the love within.* They say that *home is where the heart is.* If that is the case, then how would you know if you don't venture outside of it from time to time? In the winter of 2016, I finally returned home after traveling and working for sixteen months. Suffice to say, I was exhausted. Initially, before the year started, I wanted to reach more cities. The allure of living in many cities enticed me. However, after traveling for so long, the need to return home to reset was essential. After exploring five continents in sixteen months, I needed to regroup by *going back to the beginning.* To uncover the love within yourself, it is important to recognize that everything starts with you. It started with obtaining that courage to take that first step. Going back to the beginning allows you to tap into that foundation or the roots from which you first started; a reminder of how it all began.

» *To travel is to reach new heights.* There were many times when I stopped myself from doing something that I wanted to do. Skydiving was one of them. Sure, it is a very common bucket list item, but it meant more to me than that. You see, I don't do too well with heights, so I figured skydiving would be the next logical step. I made sure I called loved ones in case the unfortunate happened. This is a conversation excerpt with one of my best friends while I was in Mesquite, Nevada.

"I'm just calling to say goodbye," I told my friend Johnny.

No reply. Silence thickens.

"What do you mean by that?" his voice concerned.

"I mean I'm about to do something I have not done before, and if I don't make it, I wanted to make sure you know how good of a friend you are to me," I explained with sincerity.

"Okay... stop bullshitting me. What are you doing?" he shrieked back.

"Dude, it's cool. I'm just playing. I'm just going skydiving," I laughed as I broke the tension.

"Geez, you almost gave me a heart attack. I thought you were going to do something stupid... WAIT, YOU'RE DOING WHAT?!" he yelped.

Now, I probably know what you're thinking. *I am not getting on a plane and then voluntarily jumping out of it at 13,000 feet!* No, no, that is not what I am asking of you. What I do ask of you is that you try something new and different, and, no, it does not have to occur at 13,000 feet. *Why try something different?* Well, you may discover a certain bravery that wasn't there before, and when that situation calls for it... you go and take off! There's a superhero in every single one of us. Go take the plunge!

~ ~ ~

Traveling does not have to be costly or outlandish in destination. The point of it is to take a departure from your normal routines and literally jolt your mental, spiritual, and physical being every now and then. The beauty of traveling is about discovering new environments and exploring the outside world as well as within. The world is your classroom. Learn from it.

GO AND GET OUT THERE!!!

"We travel not to escape life,
but for life not to escape us."
—ANONYMOUS

ACTION STEPS

- Plan one new trip in your city or state. Then plan a new trip in another state you have not been to before. A week is recommended for both.

- Plan one new trip in a different country. Yes, you can start with Canada or Mexico.

- Jot down things you have learned at each new place as well as things you have learned about yourself through the process.

- Plan to wander using all five senses. Write down not just what you see, but also what you hear, smell, taste, and feel. You'll be amazed at what you will discover.

Your thoughts. Your roadmap. Your next steps...

_____

_____

_____

_____

_____

_____

_____

_____

_____

_____

_____

_____

_____

_____

_____

_____

_____

_____

_____

Chapter 4

Love

One of the key ingredients of *Thrive Medicine* is this very subject. It contributes to the driving force and the constitution of the *why* in your overall life purpose. Love has been written about for centuries in various mediums and will always be sought after. Or does it have to be something that you need to seek out? Can it also be manifested from within as well? Love comes in many different forms besides romantic love, even though that is the most common love that we seek. Sometimes, love does not have to show up in another person.

Wonder, curiosity, and excitement graced her face as she stepped onto the crowded streets of Times Square, NYC. The city hailed as the "greatest city on Earth" and "the city that never sleeps" definitely did not disappoint that night. The air that Friday night was crisp and refreshing, to say the least.

No. Who am I kidding?! She was freezing her butt off!

Being a native from the West coast, my friend was not used to the northeastern region of the country during the winter time. Having grown up in this area, I was used to it. It was the wind chill that added that special touch of frigid, making it feel like twenty degrees out when it was, in fact, closer to the upper thirties. Nevertheless, all that did not stop her from soaking in all the energy that Times Square produces. And it can give a lot. Arianna's face was mesmerized by it all.

This was a rarity for me, however. To be able to tour someone who had never been to New York City, ever?! *What do you do first? Where do you take a newbie? How do you go about a city that holds eight million people?*

Well, I thought to myself, *I could make up a list or just go with it.* As an avid traveler myself, I enjoy keeping a balance between planning and spontaneity, hanging onto the mystery that comes with discovering new experiences. Therefore, I took her requests of what she wanted to see into consideration and added some of my own. We trekked towards the *"touristy"* locales first: the awe-inspiring Central Park to the jaw-dropping views of the nighttime skyline on top of Rockefeller Center to the darting taxicab rides. But her favorite? The *underground subway.*

I was scratching my head as I looked at her blankly. *You're kidding me, right?*

"Why the subway?" I curiously asked her.

"Well, to me, it is so vast and complex, and everything still works at the same time. Plus, it amazes me how beautiful it is to see all these people going about their day, but not noticing they're in this organized chaos," she giggled to herself.

That laugh. And the little tears that came from those laughs.

I could have listened to that laugh all day. What you do not know is that there is another layer to all of this. *My unyielding love for her.* We had only met less than a year before when I was working at a clinic in

Nevada. We met in a Latin dance class. I thought that, as a Chinese-American, picking up some rhythm might actually do me some good. Back in college, I tinkered around with salsa dancing, studied abroad in Spain, and even witnessed Flamenco dancing, which took my understanding of dancing to another level. So, going into that night's class, I was sure I would have no problem.

Except for one thing...

No one told me that I was going to meet *her* that night. A striking beauty with gentleness to match and a contagious laughter is what drew me to her. Suffice to say, I fell hard that night. The second time in my life.

"First time here?" she asked as I tripped over myself.

"Is it that obvious?" I snickered.

"Well, it is pretty straightforward. It's one-two, one-two..." she instructed. Her voice gradually trailed off.

Well, like all things that are too good to be true, I had to fall back to Earth pretty quickly. Much to my dismay, she was already seeing someone. *Yes, I heard the glass break in my head too.*

Fast forward a few months, a handful of outings together, and a big leap of faith to come to the East coast, and now, here we are, on the streets of Manhattan, together. Now, I can probably guess what you are thinking to yourself: *Such foolishness and naivety. What are you doing wasting your time?* No matter how many times I try to cover it up, I will always be a *hopeless romantic.* However, at this point, as challenging as it may seem to be with a woman who is already with someone else, I stumbled upon a vital realization from my travels.

One of the secrets to *thriving* is to focus on the things you do have as opposed to the things you do not have.

I remember feeling so much heartache afterwards because a person that I loved was unavailable and there was nothing that I could do about it. This took me a long while to get over, to process and understand how it applied to the bigger picture in my life.

There are many times we as humans easily fall into the trap of looking at the person next to us and feel envious of what they have—whether it is a new car, a new job, the next smartphone, the list goes on, but it is also endless. Why would you *want* all these things? You have everything you *need* in life. When you focus on things you do have in your life, such as family, friends, important role models, your health, etc., gratitude is manifested. Gratitude supersedes our desires for temporary things and events. Love for me was awareness + appreciation + gratitude.

In addition, it is also important to recognize when certain things are not meant for you, and the need to just let it go and appreciate what you are able to have, no matter how temporary it may be. You may call it destiny, fate, or whatever, but people come into your life for a reason. Whether it creates a positive or negative experience, the lesson needs to be understood in order to not repeat certain missteps in your life. I also believe there is something beautiful that comes out of every experience, whether we recognize or not. It is developing that keen sense of *awareness* in order to pick up the lessons and the *beauty*. This takes practice. I strive to do it every day. Or else, we can get caught in the vicious cycle of repeating detrimental mistakes over and over again. Divorces, arguments, chronic health problems: any of these ring a bell?

The biggest lesson that I took from spending this precious time with my friend was that even though I did indeed love her, I was more than satisfied with *nothing* in return. To me, that was *love*. Having no expectations or outcomes from intended actions allowed me to enjoy my moments with her that much more. The gift of giving and sharing. In my case, it was sharing my time with someone special.

It is the very experience that enriches us, not things.

When we are born into this world, we come in with nothing. As we eventually depart this world, we will also leave with nothing. We cannot take "things" with us. We can only bring memories and experiences. These constitute love: living a life fully intentioned. Going into this practice with that kind of mindset will lift you out of the cycle of wanting something in return. Let's try an exercise:

» Do you remember your favorite childhood memory? Describe the details.

» Do you remember your first kiss? How did it make you feel?

» What about when your first child was born? Tell me the emotions that came with that event.

What did all of these experiences do for you? How did they elevate your life?

I encourage you to write down the answers to these questions and reflect on them. Dig deep and explore the most significant events that have caused the greatest changes within you, whether they were positive or negative, and always ask *why* and *how* they changed you. The very motion of writing these experiences down and actually reliving them will reinforce why you are here and why you wake up in the morning. It is the realization of how much the human spirit can tolerate and persevere through. It is because you are an amazing human being!

So, what about unconditional love? What does that actually mean?

Now, I am not a relationship expert or a love guru but, to me, unconditional love is the non-judgmental approach of treating everything and everyone of equal value. It is the exercise of accepting conditions and people just as they are and appreciating their existence.

Confused? Well, I didn't say this was easy. Let's take a simple analogy. Picture your dog. Don't have one? Then, borrow your neighbor's. Got him? Okay, imagine this:

Let's say you go to work with high intentions of making it a great day. There is gridlock traffic in the morning, someone cuts you off, and there is already a stack of paperwork as you arrive at your desk. Lunchtime rolls around and your boss hands you more work to do. Three arguments around you ensue as you attempt to calm down your coworkers. You miss your lunch and finish your day back in rush hour before arriving home to your dog waiting for you.

Feeling a little irritated? Maybe a little angry as you arrive home? What else are you feeling? Okay, now back to your dog. How do you think your dog will respond to you? Will your dog *judge* you if you are angry, irritated, or just hating your job? Will your dog *judge* you or look at you in a certain way if you thought less of yourself or did not have enough self-esteem at that particular moment?

No. Your dog is *pure love.* It is *unconditional.* He shows up for you no matter what, not when the conditions are right for him. *Your dog just simply shows up.* It may seem like a weird analogy, but practice showing up for your husband, mother, neighbor, teacher, granddaughter, friend, or coworker just because you simply can. That is love. We are all love for each other. We are all manifestations of love. Just show up. The rest will follow.

> *"Your heart is like that magical kitchen.*
> *If you open your heart, you already have*
> *all the love you need."*
> — DON MIGUEL RUIZ

So, what about self-love?

This is probably an essential gift you can give not just yourself, but also to others. Self-love is the practice of recognizing and acknowledging yourself. Recognize that you are human and everything that comes with being human, including the light and dark sides. Acknowledge your existence and realize its connection to everyone and everything else. Accept that you are beautiful no matter the "story" you tell yourself or what anyone outside of you says. Accept that you are already *perfect* because you simply *exist* in this world.

Another way to look at this is to assess where you are at, at this specific point in your life:

1. How do you feel when you are with others? Do you crave attention or tend to shy away due to what others may perceive of you?

2. Do you tend to lean towards solitude, or prefer to generally spend most of your time with others because you feel lonely?

3. When you are with your significant other, do you tend to follow what they say, even if it puts you in an uncomfortable position? Or do you find yourself blaming your partner for everything that goes wrong?

The purpose of self-love is not to be *selfish* with just yourself. The idea is to fill your own "gas tank up," so you have the ability to share yourself with others without feeling depleted or robbed from. With regard to love, I prefer to use the phrase "sharing yourself" instead of "giving yourself." What I mean by this is when you understand just how INCREDIBLE you are, you will be filled with contentment with everything that has transpired in your life and what you actually have. You will also realize that there is nothing else on this planet that will provide you with what you *need*, except you. This is where *self-esteem* and *self-worth* come from: SELF, THAT MEANS YOU! And it can only come from you. From nowhere else and from no one else.

Once your "tank" is filled with self-love and understanding, then you will acknowledge that *it is not something to give, but to share.* Once you do that, your world will change.

How do you practice love?

Simply put, every day. In every action. In every moment. *Start by practicing non-judgement.* Strive to understand that *nothing* in life is really in our control. The only thing we have control over is how we react to our outside world. This includes how we communicate with people, how we deal with trauma and events, and how we cannot change the things around us, but to just accept them as they are.

Continue being kind no matter what. Even when you believe certain people do not deserve it. By being a *leader*, you will set a different example to those who have practiced negativity and misery upon others. Just by elevating your energy, you will instantly give them a different outlook. Showing that, instead of *misery loves company, misery cannot sustain company.*

The concepts of gratitude and appreciation, unconditional love, and self-love are noted here to re-emphasize the fact that love comes in many different forms besides romantic love. It teaches you the value of simply accepting what you have. Love exists without conditions. You are truly enough, no matter how the outside world views you. This all converts merely surviving to *thriving!*

Meanwhile, back in New York, it was the end of Arianna's long weekend trip. Snow had fallen. Famous NYC Pizza was savored, twice! Museums were visited. Simply put, another part of her world had unfolded, and even talks about a repeat trip had started. As I shuttled her back to the airport to catch her afternoon flight, I couldn't help but wonder if we were ever going to see each other again. Many months had already passed since we last saw each other, and our lives continued to move on. Even though she and I carried on in our own paths, every time we had a chance to connect, it was as if we just picked up where we left off.

Newark Liberty Airport was quite busy at the time, being the holiday season. Lines stretched from end to end in a snake-like, chaotic fashion. As I was escorting her through the security line that led to the airline gates, I noticed she was holding my arm as firmly as she could. She then gazed up at me.

"I don't know how to thank you enough for being so wonderful towards me this weekend," she exclaimed. "I can't believe I was here. The experience would have never been the same without you." I could feel excitement radiating from her.

The lines shortened, and our steps inched closer. Right before the gate, I turned to her. I could feel the nerves revving throughout my entire body. Then, suddenly, a certain calmness took over. I took a deep breath...

"Do you want to know why?" I asked her. Her eyes locked onto mine. "It's because I simply *love* you. I always have, and I always will."

Her large brown eyes gasped. She was speechless. Before she had a chance to respond, I quickly embraced her. It was the type of embrace to communicate to her that *this is until the next time we see each other again.* We held on tightly as if time had stopped for us.

She stepped onto the escalators that led towards the gate. Now, in my head, every great romantic comedy would have ended with the couple walking away from one another. Then, they would turn around and run towards each other with an attempt to kiss but, instead, their foreheads would collide. Yes, I know. I'm a total dweeb.

Instead, as she slowly rose up, almost out of my line of sight, something else happened. As our eyes met one last time, a smile flashed across her face. She was silent, but I heard her heart smile back at me.

ACTION STEPS

- Express yourself differently than you have done in the past. Instead of acquiring things, why not just try showing up for people? Your presence is enough.

- Listening is an unbelievable skill that reinforces the connection in relationships.

- Write down what you desire in an ideal partner and in an ideal relationship.

- Write down things that can help improve your self-worth. Focus on what is amazing about you, not what you believe is attractive to others.

Your thoughts. Your roadmap. Your next steps...

Chapter 5

Gratitude

"In the end, only three things matter: how much you loved, how gently you lived, and how gracefully you let go of things not meant for you."
— BUDDHA

Growing up in a developed nation such as America, it can be very easy to take the luxuries available to us for granted while others struggle to survive. The opportunity to travel and witness others living in their own environment, society, and culture helps bridge that gap. Seeing that struggle may make us feel alone, but we are really in this together. It just takes perspective, but more importantly than that, it takes gratitude. Gratitude is a key ingredient of *Thrive Medicine* because in order to know where you want to go, you must understand the sanctity of life surrounding all of us. Personally, I did not appreciate the value of common household items and utilities such as electricity, a washer and dryer, or hot running water until I traveled to the Dominican Republic.

"So, how many supplies do we have?" asked Jeff. "Do you think we will have enough for this trip?"

"We will have to see. I still have to go to another pharmacy on my way back. I heard the pharmacist has been gathering drugs for us for a couple of weeks," I replied.

It was our spring break from medical school in the summer of 2008. Some of us had decided to use our free time to visit exotic vacation locations. Others had chosen to go back home. I decided to go to the Dominican Republic with my team to assist in the underserved community of *Neyba*. We needed to acquire certain amounts of medications and supplies to bring for the residents. Some of the residents had never seen a doctor in their lives. We had also brought donated clothes and toiletries.

To say we were excited about this medical mission trip is a complete understatement. There were about twenty of us who decided to team up for this mission. Most of us were student doctors with a handful of practicing supervising physicians. A few of us were medical technicians, some had nursing experience. The purpose of the trip was to deliver healthcare to a more remote area. This involved the assistance of a local community outreach organization, which was also involved with community rebuilding and education. What I did not anticipate was the mission's profound effect on my life perspective.

Four days into our mission, we were able to see and treat about a thousand patients. Most of them were women, small children, and infants. Some of the diseases and conditions we came across included, but were not limited to, fungal infections of the skin, malnutrition, and acute bacterial pneumonia. We had one special case with a five-year-old who had an abnormal heart sound. This is called a heart murmur, and it just so happened he had a ventricular heart defect as well. He needed a heart valve replacement. Through a few quick calls, the child was fortunate enough to have an expedited surgery in Santo Domingo, the country's capital.

We worked long and arduous ten-hour days. Droves of patients lined up down the road. As volunteers, we did not accept any payment for our services. However, many of the patients graciously thanked us and came bearing gifts. The gifts were either handmade trinkets or homegrown food. I felt very humbled. At the time, as a student physician, I had very limited live patient experience, so to be treating this third-world population was a very profound experience.

While there, I realized how much I took hot showers and electricity for granted back home. The compound we lived on had backup generators. Every so often, they would kick on due to the lack of running electricity during the evenings. During the days, I saw faces of the locals. They were faces requesting help for they had no options for medical care. Elements of a hard life had weathered many of them. Even after waiting at least three to four hours to be seen, the locals did not complain or pour out their problems to us. They simply told their *stories* of how they lived. Most of this came from their body language. They did not have to go into depth. Their mannerisms painted a landscape of their lives, usually within a ten-minute patient encounter. I loved every minute of it. This confirmed why I had walked this path. All of my own issues paled in comparison to what these villagers went through.

~ ~ ~

Gratitude as a strategy for *thriving*:

» **Gratitude is an acknowledgment of others.** We must recognize there are approximately seven billion people (and counting) on this planet. That is a lot of people. We must acknowledge we must depend on each other as well as live with one another. Challenges arise when people adopt a "you vs. me" mentality. We are struggling to survive when there is a "what is mine and not yours" way of thinking. This leads to social isolation and disharmonious relationships. When Earth is viewed from space, there are no borders that separate us. When we are *thriving*, we recognize that we are not the only ones living on this planet. When we are *thriving*, we acknowledge the existence of other human beings. When we are *thriving*, we realize that we need to depend on each other to live well and to live deeply.

» *Gratitude is an appreciation of others.* To give gratitude to another is to recognize and to thank another person's efforts and the time they dedicated to the task at hand. Whether it is as simple as holding another's hand to cross the street or as complex as rebuilding a house after hurricane Katrina. To give thanks is to recognize that the person could have spent their energy and time doing something else when, instead, they decided to assist you.

» *Gratitude serves to strengthen bonds.* When we fail to recognize each other's existence in this world, we fail to see the greatness in each other. Take for example, street artists in the city. Ever stop and gaze in awe in their artwork or performance? Stopping to tip them is one thing, but taking the time to acknowledge that person's work is priceless. The process of acknowledgment strengthens the bonds between humans because it taps into a creative part that has been or has yet to be manifested in yourself. It is relatable. Gratitude allows us the chance to appreciate each other, even for a few moments. Gratitude gives us the opportunity to convey thoughts of appreciation when time can be fleeting, when we don't get many opportunities to do so. That artist's work is greatness manifested. This is in all of us.

Fast forward eight years. I find myself working with the Veterans of the United States Armed Services in New Orleans, Louisiana.

During that time, there was an outpatient clinic that offered primary care services in addition to sub-specialty services. Working with veterans was an interesting experience for me. They were a diverse population of men and women who had sacrificed much. Not only had they sacrificed their time and energy but, for some, their lives. Some came out of their military service with leg amputations, some with post-traumatic stress disorder, and others with chronic pain.

I had one patient who came to me with chronic neck pain. This particular patient, as per their medical records, was noted to be a high suicide risk. Like with others before him, from a clinical perspective, we are expected to be alert and vigilant with patients who have abused pain medications. At first, this patient did not strike me as someone who could be trusted. Checking his record further, he had tested positive in a drug urine test for marijuana. I mentioned this to him.

"I've been clean for nearly two years now. Do you know how hard it is to live like this, day-in and day-out with this much pain?" his voice filled with despair.

This patient had a neck spinal fusion a few years back and did try many other alternative modalities for pain control such as physical therapy, yoga, and acupuncture.

"I'm just tired of suffering like this, doctor. I try every day to do my routine exercises in the morning, to stretch and to relax the best way that I can. But I've been living like this for about five years now. I understand doctors don't like to give out narcotics for fear of abuse," he exclaimed.

"I hear you. I do, Mr. Smith," I replied. His tired eyes gazed at his weathered hands. His face appeared as if he'd trekked far to get to the clinic. There was a large portion of our veterans who were also homeless. Most would stay at the nearby park just outside the clinic.

"First, Mr. Smith, I just want you to be safe, but at the same time, I do not want you to suffer. As long as you work with me, I will do my best to relieve your pain," I reassured him, and prescribed him a safe and appropriate amount of medication in addition to behavioral health therapies.

He nodded in agreement.

A couple of days later after that visit, my nurse handed me a handwritten letter. I opened it up and read its contents:

"Because others would not treat my pain. They look at my labels: high blood pressure, mental state, suicidal; they can look at these labels and tell there's no fixing me. A 25-cent pill is my life. I can't stand to be me and be called a drug addict. FYI, if you didn't give me pain relief, I had a plan to join the 13 vets a day that take their life. Thank you. You gave me hope. At least I'm not suffering a thousand screams of hell for 4 hours a day."

~ ~ ~

Another way to think about *gratitude* is that it does not have to come in the form of gifts. Sometimes a handwritten card delivers the same heartfelt impact, if not more than a tangible gift. A gift purchased with money can be easily accomplished, but to express gratitude by writing thoughts down conveys a different feeling.

Let's try an exercise:

> **Are there people in your life who have made an impact on you?**
>
> **What do you have in your life that you are thankful for?**

» *Write random thank you cards.* Write thank you notes on Post-it notes and leave them in arbitrary places. This may seem random because it is, but the point of this is to thank others, even when it is unwarranted. We all need to feel appreciated, and we all need to give appreciation to others.

» *Thank a teacher or a mentor*. If you had the good fortune of having an inspirational person in your life, thank them. Without them, you would have had a more challenging time pushing yourself to achieve your goals or dreams. It does not matter if this was a paid position or if someone had volunteered their time. These people dedicated their time and energies to convey a message or lesson to you. To teach someone in their own inspirational way has an exponential effect. Once a lesson is passed on, it has a multiplicative effect of reaching out to many others.

» *Thank a family member*. Sure, you share blood with them, but family members are not necessarily bound to help you out in life. For those of us that are lucky to have close bonds with a family member, thank them. For those of us that are lucky to have family members that have participated in our lives, thank them.

» *Thank strangers*. You may ask, "Why would I ever thank a stranger?" Well, remember that we live with seven billion others. Believe or not, we are connected in more ways than one. We have an influence on each other whether we are cognizant of this or not, so why not thank them? A stranger built the house you live in and the car you drive. A stranger built that coffeehouse you frequent every morning. So, give back by donating time to an urban community garden. Help build a home that others have lost due to a natural disaster. Give time to an elderly resident in a nursing home who has no family members. Give thanks to a perfect stranger who shared an insightful conversation over coffee. Thank the wedding planners and the party hosts for giving you an awesome wedding experience! You get the idea. Go give gratitude without expecting anything in return.

Are you getting the drift?

A part of *thriving* is recognizing the interconnection between us humans. One way of recognizing this is by using gratitude. Gratitude is more than a simple "thank you." It is an impactful imprint. We can take experiences and memories with us, and they will have a more indelible impression on our lives than actual things do. By giving gratitude, you are appreciating those experiences. Those experiences and memories, whether positive or negative, left an impression and helped shape who you are today. Your life has come to this very juncture due to the collective experiences and choices you have made. Gratitude reinforces the acknowledgment of those choices, and that is a beautiful thing.

**Thank you. Gracias. Danke. Obrigado. Grazie.
Merci. Natick. Tack. Mahalo. 謝謝.**

ACTION STEPS

- Give random gratitude in the form that is unique to you.

- Thank others before you and others after you.

- Create a nightly bedtime routine of what you are thankful for. Let's do that right now, write it down. *What are you thankful for?*

- Gratitude is more than a gift and a simple verbal expression. Volunteer your time or energy towards a person, community, or a cause you believe in. Impact others.

Your thoughts. Your roadmap. Your next steps...

_____

_____

_____

_____

_____

_____

_____

_____

_____

_____

_____

_____

_____

_____

_____

_____

_____

_____

Chapter 6

Forgive

"You will forgive them not because they deserve to be forgiven, but because you don't want to suffer and hurt yourself every time you remember what they did to you."
— DON MIGUEL RUIZ, AUTHOR OF *THE FOUR AGREEMENTS*

A few years ago, I attended a very curious conference…

The conference room was chilling and barren, or at least that was how I felt when I entered it on that sunny afternoon in southern California. In the past, I was used to attending conferences on topics like food or medicine, but this was something I had not attended before—a seminar on *personal change*. One could argue that things like this are a bunch of hoopla. As far as I can remember, I have always been personally fascinated with the self-improvement arena. There is something to be said for fostering that hidden motivation to change something in your life; a realization that how you were living had not been working for you; deciding to seek something different and some guidance on it. At that time in my life, I was ready to invite change. However, I was not prepared for what I was about to experience...

After a day of vigorous exercises, we moved onto a very tender subject, *forgiveness*. At first glance, it seemed like it would not be a big deal to discuss. I thought to myself, *What is it that I cannot forgive that I need to?* I had no enemies and it was not typical of me to hold grudges. As the moderator commenced this segment of the program, she told us to find a spot on the floor and asked us to sit comfortably.

"This may be a challenging exercise for some of you. The whole point of this is to be able to let go of that *emotional plug*—the plug that holds us back from moving forward with our lives."

She proceeded to tell us to close our eyes and to imagine a lush garden, one that humans had hardly touched. In order to get there, we would have to enter a stairwell and slowly descend down until the light from this lush garden unraveled itself. Having my eyes closed up until this point, I was traveling with a certain trepidation.

I was entering into the unknown.

The garden suddenly appeared before me. It was a gorgeous sight to behold. A lime green pasture sat next to a gentle brook under the warm and encompassing branches of several oak trees. I could smell nearby honeysuckle as my mind continued to wander. There, on an old bedrock, sat a male infant, probably no more than three months old. I thought, *why is there a baby in my vision?* As I approached the rock and the sitting cooing baby, my mind began to scurry, trying to figure out who this baby was. Then, it finally dawned on me.

This was my *father*.

As I tried to piece together why my consciousness decided to bring my father here, no less this much younger version of him, I recalled all of our past encounters together. My father and I did not have the best relationship. When I think about what a stereotypical father-son relationship would be like, I think of a father teaching his son how to deconstruct a car, about deciphering the mysteries of the opposite gender, or of a father doing his best to simplify what he knows about *life* in general. I did not have that relationship growing up. Mine was stricken with disappointment, emotional abandonment, and neglect. My father was physically present in my life, just not emotionally and mentally—areas where I needed him the most. Growing up in a Chinese household, the area that he focused most on was academics and he wanted me to achieve the best by any means possible. This was where my unforgiveness was rooted.

I watched the younger version of my dad cooing and laughing at me, and I just could not help but smile. As I continued to smile and laugh with him, I started to see flashes of people behind him, sort of like a visual flickering of an analog radio, adjusting to find the right station. One was of his mother, who did not have a close relationship with him. Another was his own father, whom I have never met and understand that he passed when my father was sixteen. The last flash was of my dad as an adult. He appeared with his hands in his pockets, peering down, looking at his younger self. He looked sullen and quiet. As if about to start a solo journey, he took a quick look, turned his back towards the baby, looked out into the horizon, and started to walk towards it. Probably something he had done many times before. There, like a lightning strike, it dawned on me.

He was *alone*.

He had been alone for most of his life. He lived in solitude without close parental love and was also an only child. The person he is today suddenly all made sense. How he had expressed his misguided anger and neglect towards me finally made sense. He never really received enough *love.*

Unexpectedly, my resentment disappeared. Instead, I began to empathize with that loneliness, that feeling of isolation. As I gazed at the baby and the adult version of my father, tears rolled down my eyes like gentle raindrops off leaves. At that moment, I felt a certain closeness to him that I had not felt before. I acquired an overall sense of understanding that, due to the lack of guidance growing up, he was the father he could be based on his experiences and what he knew. At that instance, my body started to feel lighter as if an enormous amount of weight had been lifted off my chest. My eyes slowly opened... *unforgiveness* was no longer in my vocabulary.

~ ~ ~

Forgiveness can be a very personal subject for some people. It can be very challenging to let go of what has happened in the past. The pain accumulated since that initial trauma can really build up and fester if not taken care of properly. This was a life-changing moment because it allowed me to go very deep into why I was growing this hatred and anger inside of me. What set this moment apart from just superficially understanding the concept of *forgiveness* was the fact that I explored and spent time digging. I dug up what was submerged to understand where these roots were coming from and how it applied, even threatened, other parts of my life. By empathizing with this notion and with my own father, I was able to break free from the bonds that held me back from living, from *thriving.*

And so, the whole idea of forgiveness is that *it is not about them so much as it is about you.*

Wait, it's not about them?

Simple answer? No.

When you decide to forgive someone or something, you subsequently let go of whatever it is you are attached to, whether it is anger, resentment, or hate. When you forgive, it is not necessarily that the person or that event deserves it, but rather you are giving permission to liberate yourself from the attachment, to break free from the chains that have locked you down. This *specific* attachment has kept you from moving on or moving forward with your life.

Let's use some examples:

» Not forgiving an ex-girlfriend/boyfriend for cheating, thus preventing you from starting a new relationship.

» Not forgiving your best friend for betrayal, thus creating lost time between you and them.

» Not forgiving yourself for embarrassment, thus preventing you from making it to your acting audition.

» Not forgiving yourself for not following your passions, thus preventing you from switching careers.

» Not forgiving your coach for mistrust, thus preventing you from reaching the national team.

» Not forgiving your brother for being irresponsible, thus preventing you from trusting others.

One can easily come up with any example and have a certain negative feeling towards it. The sticking point is having the audacity to let go of that *emotional plug* that continues to draw energy from you, such as anger, resentment, hate, or disappointment. These are *emotional energy sucks*. I like to call them that because they inhibit you from marching forward. They leave you *fatigued and exhausted and drained*, thereby keeping you from *thriving*. If you do not give the opportunity to forgive, then you will be carrying around a "weight" that will drag you down.

Why is it difficult for some of us to forgive then?

Let's break this down. There is a certain amount of investment that we place in people or life events. Not so much money, but the "currency" of *time* and *emotional energy* and, with this, certain expectations. Let's consider a very best friend relationship or a significant other. When we arrive at a moment where there is a break of trust or betrayal, it produces an emotional response in the form of an argument, for instance. This is normal because, as human beings, this is part of our make-up. However, when this starts to become an issue for some is when the emotional response lingers and halts you from opening up in another part of your life. This is what we mean by the *emotional plug*. A term coined by the late author and speaker Debbie Ford.

Therefore, at this junction, you have two choices:

Let it consume you,

or

forgive yourself and let it go.

You, and you alone, have the power to decide this. You are THAT powerful.

It took me many years to be able to forgive my father. I spent a lot of time resenting him, but did not realize it was misdirected. I ended up being sucked into a victim cycle where his parents were absent for him and he was that for me. Earlier, when I was unaware of this cycle that I was caught up in, I asked myself, "What is it that I had done that would provoke such anger in my father to treat me like that?" It took some time for me to understand that sometimes people do not know what they are *doing*, especially in the context of how they treat others. They do not know they are hurting themselves. They do not understand that certain issues that have yet to be resolved on the inside do, indeed, manifest and project outwards onto others. When this happens, it can be very dangerous. Think about a snowball effect or a domino effect. When you pass on your misery to someone else unknowingly, then that person may do the same to someone else (domino effect). Thereby, the misery can reach two people, then each of them passes it onto two more people, becoming four then eight then sixteen (snowball effect). Imagine this cycle never ending. On the other hand, imagine you STOPPING this vicious cycle.

> **Another powerful tool I would like to share with you is this: *release your forgiveness.***

You can pursue this in two ways: either forgiving that person, thing, or event in-person, OR forgiving out loud. Both are equally effective.

When I decided to face my father and tell him how I felt growing up, I received a raised eyebrow. He presumed that I received a very "normal" childhood—a roof over my head, food on the table, clothes on me and my sister's backs. And in many respects, those were appreciated, and I thanked him for that. It was the other things that I was missing from my "normal" childhood. After hearing me out, whether he completely understood or apologized after the fact was not the point. The point was that he *listened* and that I forgave him.

In this example, my father is the person in which I am forgiving. For you, how the opposite person responds might be different. The key is that it *does not matter* how they respond. It matters that you opened yourself up and chose to release that emotional plug. The whole intention is for you to *choose* to forgive and to *release* it out. The rest is secondary.

The second approach may be used if you are having a challenging time facing that person, object, or event in question to forgive. For example, if someone has already passed on, then release it by forgiving ***out loud***. You might write a letter, journal, record a voice memo, or record footage of yourself forgiving out loud. Either way is fruitful in giving you the chance to let it go. You can do this by speaking into that recorder as if you are directing yourself towards that person. It is more efficacious that way and more potent for you.

Remember that you DESERVE less suffering and more *thriving*. Remember that it is about releasing these *emotional energy sucks*. Forgiveness is about being ready to move forward with your life; getting ready to *thrive*.

"It is only when we have the courage to face things exactly as they are without self-deception or illusion that a light will develop out of events by which the path to success may be recognized."
— I CHING

ACTION STEPS

- Write down what you need to forgive and why.

- Forgive in person.

- Forgive via letter, song, recording, or by whatever means feels right.

- Most importantly, forgive yourself. List things you forgive yourself for.

- What is not forgiving certain things, events, or people preventing you from doing?

- Write down the next steps in releasing that emotional bond.

Your thoughts. Your roadmap. Your next steps...

Chapter 7

Inspire

"I trust that the universe doesn't want us to fail so it gives you angels and support systems to support when you commit to your calling and purpose."
— DOMINICA ZHU

The ability to tweak someone's life path for the better makes all the difference. It essentially takes a simple push. When someone is receptive and open to the possibilities of changing the course of their lives, you follow through. That is inspiration. That is support. That is *thriving*. The following is a snippet of a conversation with one of my good friends about the course of his professional future.

"I changed my career path because of you."

Three years ago, I asked my friend Rick, "Are you picking obstetrics for you or for someone else?" Rick is one of the most selfless people I know. He has a very loving relationship with his family and his close friends. He has always been a "take the shirt off his back for others" type of guy. Being selfless as he is, I could tell he had trouble tackling this juncture in his life.

It was a late fall evening and I was about to turn into bed when my good friend called and made this confession to me. We spent many summers together talking about the most recent professional basketball game, women, and Eskrima (filipino martial arts). You know, typical guy stuff. Rick is the son of a dentist and started his professional career in nursing before pursuing medicine. We had conversed many times about the ins-and-outs of healthcare and its ever-changing landscape in our current era. Still, it was something he could see himself doing every single day. He was a very cordial and fun-loving guy, and we had the best times playing on the basketball courts in the Jersey humid heat when we were younger.

I stopped what I was doing. "Wait... what do you mean?" I asked, perplexed.

"Well, I took your advice and chose a different route for myself. I went into family medicine, instead of obstetrics and gynecology," he replied.

Rick was pursuing obstetrics with his then fiancée, who, I found out on the same call, he was no longer with. His ex-fiancée was pursuing OB and he joined her in applications, and even looked at different parts of the country where they could match residencies together. At that time, I felt a hesitation and reluctance in his voice with the whole process, and I later asked him, "Is it the process you're concerned about, or do you feel this is not something for you?"

"I'm not sure," his voice uncertain. "I thought this was, but lately, I've been feeling bothered by it."

Without intruding too much on his personal space or in his relationship with his fiancée, I simply shared some thought-provoking comments: "It is hard enough to pursue medicine in general, let alone pick the right specialty. We have to put many years of blood, sweat, and tears into this. However, if you do not pick the right

specialty, you will create needless suffering for yourself,"
I stated. I left off with Rick three years ago, not sure
what he would choose to do.

"Remember our call three years ago?" he asked.
"Well, I took some time to really think about what you
said, and I changed paths. I realized it was not something
that I wanted, but something I chose for someone else.
It was not as simple as choosing what was for dinner or
buying a new car. This had more of a lasting effect," he
said with a deep exhale as if it had been weighing down
on him and he'd finally let go.

"I understand. So, how do you feel now? You think
you made the right decision?" I asked curiously.

"Amazing. When I made the choice, everything
opened up for me. I ended up going into a training
program I fell in love with. Everyone there treats me
very well. I just wanted to thank you is all."

"You're welcome. I was just being a friend. You just
needed to be asked the *right questions,*" I replied.

Inspiration, to me, is a well-practiced endeavor that leads others
to their own truth and path. It is a selfless act and, in the end, also
produces its own rewards. The joy of it comes from witnessing
others create their own ideas and pursue their own dreams. It was
not that long ago, six years to be exact, when I felt I was living
someone else's story. At first, I was totally unaware of this. With
the guidance of others that I trusted, I understood that it was
okay to be myself and to live life how I wanted to. Writing my
own story proved to be the most powerful force that propelled
me into the next chapter of my life. Since then, I find it to be
more effortless when I am authentic and simply just living my
life to the fullest. Also, by living your life truthfully and honestly,
you indirectly give permission for others to do the same, thereby
creating a ripple effect.

How does one do that? When you make the choice to live
for yourself, little by little, the true version of yourself comes

out. You begin to talk differently, stand and walk differently. It becomes more natural and commonplace until you forget how you were before. When this happens, others around begin to observe. We are very curious beings and the majority of human communication is nonverbal. Watching others lead is already inherently inspirational and motivating. The greatest part of inspiring others is it is meant to be effortless.

> "Our presence automatically
> liberates others."
>
> — MARIANNE WILLIAMSON

We all have idols, role models, and heroes; people we look up to over time. A person's actions are more significant than what they have to say. Ellen DeGeneres is a clear example of someone who embodies inspiration. She has worked tirelessly as a comedian, TV show host, actor, and activist for decades in raising awareness on many issues. Most importantly, she raises awareness about promoting, quite simply, more love in others. Her popular tagline at the end of every show episode is, *"Please be kind to one another."* Over the thirteen-year history of *Ellen,* she has been able to donate over $50 million dollars to others in need. In addition, her work thus far has earned her the Presidential Medal of Freedom. This is the highest level of honor that a civilian can attain in recognition for contributions such as world peace, culture, and other national interests. However, Ellen is also courageous in taking her own personal risks. In 1997, on her own show, she revealed to the world that she is gay. Commercials were pulled, and she received harsh criticism and even death threats. However, she trucked on knowing it was something she could no longer be ashamed of anymore. She wanted to raise awareness for the homosexual teens who feel marginalized and outcasted. Her choice to simply live her own life has inspired generations.

Inspiration is an important part of *thriving* in that it reinforces the fact that whether one is cognizant of it or not, people are always observing you—through your words, actions, body language, and whether or not you have contributed to the world in some manner. It is not required of you to lend a hand or help a neighbor, but know that how you carry yourself as a person automatically affects another person. *So, why not carry yourself in a more positive light?* When you are an older sibling, your other siblings naturally look up to you. When you are a student, your peers automatically look to you. When you are part of the workforce, your coworkers depend on you to contribute to the company's overall mission.

Let's try an exercise to help further this:

1. Have you ever been inspired by something or someone? If so, please write that down and elaborate on what/who that was and how it has affected you.

2. Have you ever had the desire to teach or give back to others? Please write down in what fashion.

3. Have you ever noticed how others react to you when you are living your life to the fullest? Describe their reactions and their words.

My own inspiration and hero, as cliché as it sounds, comes from my own mother. She is not your average mother. There are traditional Chinese mothers, *tiger moms (a type of Hitler way of parenting where, for example, anything less than an "A" is considered a failure),* and then there was *my mother.* She is more of a *ninja assassin* than anything else, especially if you ever crossed her children. Sometimes, it's embarrassing to go out with her because she creates verbal arguments wherever we go—whether over a sale discount that was not properly marked on a receipt, or a dish that was not made properly, even after explaining it two to three times to the waiter. I guess most people are not used to her bluntness. *FYI: Do not mistake our directness or bluntness as being mean. We're just very Chinese (or for my non-Asian brethren, think straightforwardness Level 100)!* As a cultural group, we tend to not "beat around the bush" and we do not like bullshit. One time, when I was younger, when I got into schoolyard fights, my mother would actually go out on a limb and scold the other kids and even the principal! So, I made sure I got on her good side! At this point, you must think my mother was nuts. In a way, her behavior is her way of expressing herself. Perhaps maybe not in the most tactful way, but I still love her. The reason I mentioned she's *not your average mother* is because she is a mother, wife, sister, daughter, and a very powerful physician! A Chinese medical doctor to be exact. Growing up, I worked in and out of her office over the years, indirectly learning about acupuncture and Chinese medical theory. She has treated over 50,000 patients over her thirty-year career thus far. She is considered one of the top Chinese medical doctors in Staten Island, NY. So, you can say I was raised learning how to care for patients in a very holistic manner. This provided me a foundational direction in medicine, where I wanted to go. In her professional environment, my mother displays kindness, gentleness, compassion, and assertiveness that best describes how she treats people and practices. She has told me many times that her passion is *her patients.* I often recall one particular patient encounter during the many years that I spent working in her office:

The treatment timer went off, echoing sounds into the waiting room.
My mother (Dr. Yu) motioned me to unhook the patient in room three. His treatment was done. The patient had received electroacupuncture and was treated with a mineral heating lamp. I knocked on the door, walked in, and switched on the light. The room was warm and cozy. The patient had awoken from his slumber, which was common for most patients due to the combination of heat, silence, and relaxation as an effect of the acupuncture needles. Mr. Petersen was a regular at my mother's office with multiple ailments. He mostly came in with severe chronic back pain in

addition to osteoarthritis, which made it difficult for him to climb his own stairs in his house. He had gone to several conventional physicians on Staten Island, and had gone through the ringer with physical therapy, home exercises, and steroid injections. He told me he improved immensely as I was unhooking him. Initially, Chinese medicine was nowhere on his medical radar. Mr. Petersen had lost all hope until he stepped into my mother's office in the beginning.

"Dr. Yu, I hear that you perform miracles. I'm not too familiar with Chinese medicine, but this is my last resort. I've tried everything else," he spoke with weariness. It was his initial consultation at the time.

"Mr. Petersen, I am no miracle worker. I simply remove the blocks that prevent your own body from healing, which will enhance your body's ability to function optimally," she explained in her Chinese accent. "But, in order to do this, you have to understand and learn there are things that you do that will limit your own healing capacity." She went on to educate him about nutrition and lifestyle and how she would address his ailments.

"I thought we were concentrating on my back? I'm a little confused," he mentioned.

"The body is much smarter than we are. To heal your back, I have to address your whole body. Usually, there is more than one thing going on because everything is connected. I treat the whole person. But, I am not going to push you or hold your hand. You are in control of your health. If you are serious about your health, then stay. If not, that's okay, too," she affirmed.

Mr. Petersen stared at her blankly. It was as if this was the first time he was treated with this much sincerity and honesty. He remained pensive and hesitant at first.

"Okay, let's give it a try," he said finally with a smile. "I have nothing to lose at this point."

My inspiration from my mother did not come from her versatile knowledge of Chinese medicine or personal experiences dealing with her own health, but rather from her connection with others. Her uncanny ability to observe and relate to people infinitely increased my understanding of people, and also of myself. It was amazing to witness every time. Inspiration is a key aspect of *Thrive Medicine*—to lead others, or having the courage to follow another's set example in order to pave the way. Try being a role model in your community or social circles and note the difference amongst your peers. I personally *thrive* from inspiring others. Without a doubt, this propels me upwards and forward.

Search for your role model.

Have you ever had the chance to listen to a speaker present about a certain topic you were interested in, but they were not able to captivate you? When listening to them, how confident did you feel they knew their subject well? How certain were you that they were able to lead you? Great role models can help lead a person to change a certain aspect of their life. Chemistry and charisma can only go so far, however. A motivating role model, on the other hand, is able to uplift others by executing actions themselves, instead of just talking about them. *Actions speak louder than words, right?* Let's picture this. Would you be willing to learn from an overweight personal trainer or a fit one? Would you go to a doctor who hasn't been to medical school? Would you learn from a dancer who has never been on stage? This point is vital because we live in a world inundated with information. Find what works for you.

Learn to empower yourself.
Then empower others.

Embody the person that you would love to follow, even if no one else does, because how can others believe in you if you do not believe in yourself? Inspire by being a leader. The intention is not to garner followers, it is simply to just be yourself and to believe in what you love. When you resonate with what you do, there is the undying need to move forward and to take on challenges head-on, no matter what. Those that resonate with you will follow. It takes guts and audacity to lead as well as to follow others that lead. To empower others is to spark something in them that was not lit before. That spark is an awakening. That spark is enough to motivate someone to rise to a new occasion, whether it is to ask for a new job, to audition for a play, leave a relationship, or sign up for a marathon. To do this, however, learn to empower and inspire yourself first. You don't have to be "perfect," you just have to believe in yourself. The rest will follow.

> *"I'm more interested in live-acy rather than legacy, if there is such a word."*
> — JOHN GLENN, WAR HERO, ASTRONAUT, SENATOR

It's not important how long you live. It's more important HOW you live.

As you move forward in life, remember to always ask yourself WHY you do the things you are doing. If there is no answer to your WHY, then what is the purpose? Why even get up in the morning? This can be applied to your job, relationships, and the things you've acquired, to something as simple as why you drove down this road today. Your actions are dictated by your decisions. Your decisions are dictated by a belief. Your belief system is the construct by which you live your life. Follow your OWN beliefs and not others.

Continue to work and improve yourself.

Change is inevitable and so is the evolution of *man*. When you resist change, you are actually resisting the need to be different and grow. Adaptation is the key to progress, and progress is the key to happiness. Change is healthy and so is self-transformation. Ask yourself if you are satisfied with where you are at. What exactly do you want? That is the essence. Once you find the answer to that, then motivation will follow. Once you continually push yourself, others will follow, and they will inevitably be inspired. For me, nothing is more motivating than sparking a lightbulb or flame inside someone else. This, in turn, ignites my propeller to keep pushing forward to do more of it! Such a curious thing! *Thrive Medicine* is all about propelling forward as an individual, but also with others. Life mandates togetherness.

ACTION STEPS

- Ask why you do the things that you do.

- Break down your belief system so you understand the *why*. List your limiting beliefs and write opposing statements to them.

- Lead others by being your true self and not just to have followers. List items that YOU decided to do for yourself.

- List things you are passionate about and how it affects others.

Your thoughts. Your roadmap. Your next steps...

Chapter 8

Authenticity

"In order to create the life of our dreams, we need a strong foundation in which to build who we are and what we stand for. We build this unshakable foundation by living within the structure of our own personal integrity. When we are in our power, we are deeply rooted in our truth, which means we honor our needs, our desires, and ourselves."
— DEBBIE FORD, FOUNDER OF *THE SHADOW PROCESS*

To *thrive* is to shed oneself of all facades and masks; to expose your true self. To my culinary colleagues, it is peeling back an onion, layer by layer. To my artists, it is sculpting that masterpiece, chipping away the pieces that are not supposed to be there. *Thrive Medicine* is about using your authenticity to make an impact. My mother recounted a story about authenticity from when I was too young to remember:

> The brisk, warm summer breeze touched our faces as my mother and I strolled outside. This was our time to relax after dinner. This was also our time to connect. Usually, whenever I was at home from school, my mother and

I would spend our post-dinner time walking around our small development in central New Jersey. The developments had clean-cut green lots with two-story houses all identical to one another with the only difference that set each apart were the house numbers. It was unlike where I grew up originally, which marked how far our family had come.

Before my sister was born, my family lived in a two-room apartment in North Jersey, where, at the time, both of my parents waited tables at a nearby business hotel. Before establishing their careers, my folks worked tirelessly. My childhood was very simple, but it was colored with trucks and action figures on the floor, and afternoons watching *Inspector Gadget* and *Teenage Mutant Ninja Turtles*. Most of the time, just laughter filled the hallways and loud, robust crackles of the wok provided the soundtrack for our suppers.

As I came out of memory lane, my mother motioned to me, "Son, what are you thinking about?"

Evenings like this were precious and priceless to me. To be able to spend it with my mother was something that I found more and more fleeting due to my long years studying in medical school. Living in West Virginia was the first time I had lived so far away from home.

"Oh, nothing really, Mom. Just reminiscing about my childhood and how simple and happy I was," I said fondly.

"Yes, you were a good kid. You didn't give us much trouble," she commented.

"Don't be modest, Mom! I'm sure I gave you some grief," I contested. Suddenly, there was a shift in her voice.

"Well, when you were about one-year old, it was the most difficult, but a rewarding time in my life," she said. "It was the first time I challenged your father."

My attention focused on her as we walked past our neighbor's noisy terriers. "Can you tell me more, Mom?" I inquired.

I knew that my parents worked incessantly, my father sometimes two jobs at a time. He worked as a fishmonger and a college janitor as well as waited tables. "Finances were strained after you were born, and we worked many shifts. We had taken you to China on your first trip overseas but, little did I know, your father had plans of leaving you there," she lamented. "Your dad said that it would be best to leave you there for your grandmother to take care of you while he pursued graduate studies, planning to pick you up afterward." I could hear her voice cracking while also gaining emotional traction as if she was about to enter a boxing arena.

My mother is not a person that easily backs down from anyone, especially with things involving her children. So, it was interesting how she described this for the first time. She had said "*no*" to my father. Obviously, I never stayed in China nor was I raised by my grandmother.

"What happened that you were able to get me to come back to the states?"

"Well, I just felt a switch come on and begged your father and his cousins that this was not right. I did not want anyone raising my son besides me. I *stood up* for myself despite his reasonings. He argued that *everyone* did this, but I disagreed with him. That was the first time I stood up for myself," she stated proudly. My mother stood tall as she recalled that unforgettable moment.

"I'm proud that you did, Mom. My life could have changed in so many different directions if I had stayed. I wouldn't be the person I am today. Plus, that moment amongst others definitely made you who you are today," I said as I smiled and hugged her.

"Always stand up for yourself, son. Don't let anyone else tell you different."

These very words echo in my work ethic and passions every day. *Thriving* is about being authentic and true to yourself, but in order for that to happen, it also means standing up for what you believe in, even if others do not. This takes a certain amount of vulnerability and courage; however, true strength is born from this.

Let's try an exercise:

» What are some of the moments that you stood up for what you believed in? How did it feel when you were able to express yourself?

» Conversely, when was the last time you had something to say, but felt stifled by fear? How did it feel to feel trapped or closed in?

These are not easy questions to answer. I understand some of you may even hesitate, but I assure you that even notable figures in our history started off afraid:

Liu Xiaobo, a writer and professor, was detained in 2008 for calling for an independent legal system and an end to one-party rule in China. He was the first Chinese citizen to be awarded the Nobel Peace Prize in 2010.

Rosa Parks, an African-American civil rights activist, refused to sit in a designated seat when asked to move, thus disobeying Alabama law. Her actions led to the Supreme Court decision to ban segregation on public transportation in 1956.

As a young Pakistani woman, Malala Yousafzai survived a gunshot to the head when she plead for young girls to receive an education. In 2014, at the age of seventeen, she was awarded the Nobel Peace Prize—the youngest person to receive the award.

Three words come to mind when I ask myself those above questions:

Authenticity. Integrity. Honesty.

» *Authenticity* is the vehicle through which to be yourself. To fully express yourself at any given time. Others have called this your *truth*. There will be no one like you or as unique as you. This can also apply to your unique expression in the world. Why let it be influenced by anyone besides yourself? Your voice is so vital for the world to hear that it would be a tragedy if it was suppressed for any reason. Be the real YOU!

» *Integrity* means owning your words. Have you ever noticed that some people do not actually mean what they say? Do you tend to rely on those people? Words are *extremely* powerful, and they carry weight. Words, depending on how you choose to express yourself, can define your character. Use your words to inspire, not to harm.

» *Honesty* means more than just not lying. It conveys respect for others and, most importantly, respect for oneself. Using my mother as an example, it would be more detrimental if my mother disrespected herself by not standing firm with my father, as opposed to allowing me to stay in China. As food for thought, if you allow yourself to be dishonest with others then how long does it take before that becomes *normal* behavior? How long does it take before this becomes routine?

> *"To express oneself honestly, not lying to oneself—that, my friend, is very hard to do."*
> — BRUCE LEE

My own courage was tested a few years ago when I had to make an unbelievably difficult choice: the decision to leave my medical program. Here is an excerpt from my journal entries:

Sweat dripped down my brow. My voice shuttered as confirming thoughts crossed my mind and I made my final decision. I never saw this coming.

I had just gotten off the phone with a good friend of mine on a cool autumn evening. I had entered and matched into a medical training program where I had the opportunity to stay at my parents' home in New Jersey. A medical student matching into residencies is one of most challenging periods of a physician's career in the United States. A laundry list of criteria is used to determine an applicant's probability to *match* into a medical training program, including, but not limited to, test scores, resumes, and letters of recommendation. I matched into my second program of choice. Four months after starting that program, however, without a safety net, I decided to quit.

Now, some of you might have dropped your jaws, especially those who are familiar with this profession. Some of you may have shaken your heads in disapproval. I don't blame you. I probably would have, too. Let me explain. During that time, like any other medical intern, I was ready to take on any medical case that came my way. Hospital rounds, learning cases, and collaborative teamwork with nurses and other healthcare staff excited me. What I was not prepared for was the toxic, sometimes political drama that came with the healthcare environment. Amplifying this was the hazing-like nature of my program. I was really confused and discouraged by all this. I had sought counsel from my family and close friends to better understand my situation, but I quickly fell into *depression* with thoughts of quitting medicine altogether. I knew something had to change. I was spiritually dying.

Like I said, *I never saw this coming.*

My sister recommended a coach for me after hearing my distress. In hindsight, that particular phone call changed my life. I was out of options and just took a risk in pouring out whatever I was feeling to a total stranger. *Talk about being totally vulnerable!* I had no idea whether or not this person would judge me or, worse, talk me out of my current situation. But I knew my gut feelings were telling me that I was heading in the wrong direction and that I needed guidance. I was skeptical at first because I had never used a coach before and I didn't even know where to begin. *How does one go about describing a life crisis without sounding crazy or weak?* There were no "cries for help" in medicine. There was no one to lift you up while you were down. Looking back, doctors have no one to reach out to, and maybe this was the reason why we had been "losing a doctor a day" to physician suicide due to depression and undiagnosed mental illness according to Medscape[7].

This particular coach, whom I still use to this day, taught me the importance of embracing who you are and listening to your own voice. It is easy to lose that in the shuffle of others if we do not pay attention to it. We must also filter out other people's opinions, and respect what we have to say. Let's just say I was out of practice, so I decided to make that leap and listen to my own inner voice, trust my own intuition. The rest was history.

A part of *thriving* is the constant stream of choices that you have to make over your lifetime, whether it is for you or for someone else. Good practice is making sure each upcoming decision is what you truly desire at that moment. Some will be choices that you will make on a day-to-day basis:

What will I make for dinner? Who is going to pick up my children from soccer practice? Is it time for an oil change?

On the other hand, there are also those choices that you will make that can change the *course* of your life:

» The moment when you decide to give your life purpose and/ or direction.

» The moment you decide to give up your job that you are not passionate about.

» The moment you decide to end a disempowering relationship.

» The moment you decide to tell your parents your *truth*.

» The moment you decide to stand up for yourself.

How do you know if you made an authentic choice? After you make it, you have no regrets and second guesses about it. A self-affirming choice thrusts your life forward, not backwards. That is what *Thrive Medicine* is all about. According to my mother, it was not common for women of her generation and culture to get divorced or to stick to their opinions. I guess you could say my mother was cut from a different cloth, or maybe she just chose what she believed in.

Being authentic is essential to *thriving*. It is the glowing embers of a fire that does not die but is fueled by your willingness to be truthful to who you are and what you stand for. Make a statement. Be skeptical, but also firm in your convictions. You'll be glad that you did.

ACTION STEPS

- Write down something you have been afraid to voice, and the barriers that have prevented you from using your voice.

- What are the next steps in carrying out *your truth?* Write those down.

- Describe the *real* you. If someone had to write your grave stone, what would it say? How would you like to be remembered? Then, ask yourself, *Why am I this person now, and what can I change today?*

Your thoughts. Your roadmap. Your next steps...

Chapter 9

Obstacles

"Brick walls are there for a reason: they let us prove how badly we want things."
— RANDY PAUSCH, CARNEGIE MELLON PROFESSOR AND AUTHOR OF *THE LAST LECTURE*

Obstacles represent life's highway checkpoints. They are there to remind us there will always be challenges coming your way, whether you are ready for them or not. *Thriving* is all about getting up more times than falling; recognizing where you falter and how to change course to prevent missteps from happening again in the future. Without obstacles, we cannot grow, change, and evolve. Even obstacles can exist in the things we love to do. Here is an example from when I completed my first marathon:

Last time I checked, I don't recall being a rooster. Then why am I getting up so dang early?

I looked over to my alarm clock with one eye open. 5:37am. I had woken up even before my six o'clock alarm.

Geez, I must be crazy.

It was Saturday morning. This was one of the rare opportunities I could squeeze a long-distance practice run into my schedule. I had decided to sign up for the New York City Marathon almost three and a half months ago, and today, I was about to run one of the longest distances that I have ever run: eighteen miles. And that was not even the full marathon distance.

Unlike other seasoned runners, I was not a long-distance runner. I mainly sprinted in junior high school and currently raced mainly triathlons, which also include cycling and swimming. However, marathons and their long-standing droves of followers are cut from a different cloth. These people breathe, sweat, and bleed marathons. They pound the asphalt with fervor and they gladly come home with scars and cuts on their knees.

Me? I was happy if I could even complete the damn thing. The New York City Marathon had been on my list for a very long time. Twenty-six miles of asphalt, cobblestones, and bridges snaking through all five boroughs of nearly eight million people. But there was just one little thing...

I had never completed a marathon before.

Then why am I doing this? Oh, yeah, because *I friggin' love the challenge of it.*

My love for racing started ten years ago in 2006. I started with triathlons because I loved the diversity and dynamics of it. The fact that you have to transition from swim to cycle to run within one race without a relay team was fascinating to me. It was a sport that deeply originated from Kona, Hawaii and appealed to the young and the young at heart. I am not saying I was any good at it. There were many that were younger and older than me that beat me every time. I simply enjoyed the sheer sportsmanship of it and the pure challenge, especially the training necessary to partake in it. It was very humbling to see the young, elderly, first-timers, and veterans each step foot onto the starting line together to achieve something amazing. Since then, I've transitioned to 5Ks, 10Ks, half-marathons, mud-runs, and obstacles races as well.

Over the years, I've asked myself why I love racing so much and why it has become such a passion of mine. It serves as a mental challenge to keep me braving the elements, not just physically, but also mentally and emotionally. Racing tests me and my capacity to not give up. *Is it okay to quit in life?* You can always spend an exorbitant amount of time at the gym, but if you do not spend time testing your human spirit then you develop less resilience. Having resilience is akin to surfing. Similar to waves in an ocean, we will have big waves and we will have small waves. *The only thing that matters is how well you surf them, or if you are even willing to surf them at all.* Sometimes you will be knocked off your surfboard, but it is up to you to decide whether you want to get back on board or not. Applying that analogy to racing and to life, I realized that I had never quit or dropped out of a race. There were plenty of times when I wanted to quit during a race, but I never did.

Several thoughts run through my head on the mornings of my races:

"I am so exhausted and out of breath."

"I am not good enough."

"It's too long and too hard."

"Why is everyone better and faster than me?"

In the end, I tell myself that, yes, it was challenging, and yes, I was tired from cycling over twenty miles and then running for another six, or scaling walls sideways and ascending a vertical rope during a mud run. BUT I DO NOT QUIT. Quitting, to me, is turning back on all the hard work I put in up until race day. Quitting is choosing the easier option of relieving myself of the pain. Most importantly, when you decide not to quit, you empathize with the struggle of another person who might also be facing something just as challenging and can't quit.

~ ~ ~

The day of the marathon was one of the toughest days I have faced.

"No, quitting is not an option," I said under my breath. Mile marker twenty had just passed me.

I looked down at the passing concrete bridge, sweat dripping down my brow, as I crossed the Madison Avenue bridge on that chilly and windy November morning. Suddenly, I felt a slight twinge in my right calf and a concomitant left flank spasm. I reminded myself again that I could just drop out at any time. *Yes, that would be an easier route. This could all be over if I said so.* However, that all changed when I gazed to my left and then to my right. More than fifty thousand runners from more than a hundred countries came on that day to participate in the most unique city in the world—a city where you bring your attitude and leave your excuses at home. With twenty-six miles of supporting fans and the thousands of racers with me, I felt a surge throughout my entire body. I was running on pure HUMAN ENERGY. My desire to quit transformed into asking myself: *how can I make it to the next street and then to the next bridge?* One step at a time, one block at a time, and one mile at a time. That afternoon, I had one of the biggest grins of anyone there. I had finished with pride.

Obstacles are constant reminders that we need to push but, more importantly, of *why* we push. We push because when we doubt ourselves, we deprive ourselves of the glory that we can and are fully capable of doing the impossible. Sometimes, we call things or events that occur impossible when, in reality, *nothing is impossible.* To believe something is impossible is to not give yourself the opportunity to even try. Trying is just taking the first step. It is one step closer to beating the *impossible.* That is what *thriving* is all about.

Let's try an exercise. Take a moment with yourself. Put yourself in your workplace, living room, public library, park, or your favorite room!

What do you think or say about yourself when you are in doubt?

Here are some common obstacles or blocks that we encounter:

1. Comparing yourself to others.

2. Thinking you are not adequate or good enough.

3. Needing others' approval.

4. Striving for perfection.

Let's address these, shall we?

1. When you compare yourself to others, you take your individuality out of the equation. Remember that you are a UNIQUE and AWESOME human being. There is literally no one like you on this planet. There is no one with your specific genetic makeup, your skills, your talents, and your genius. What you decide to produce, whether it's a project, a book, a movie, a song, or anything else, you will infuse it with your own style and personality. That is the beauty of the human race. There is such diversity on this planet that, even though there are similarities, no one can do what you can do. Allow yourself to express your genius. The world deserves to hear from you.

2. Thinking I am not good enough is one of the biggest walls I personally have faced in the past, and one I hear often. This has a lot to do with how you were raised and the environment that you grew out of. Society can often be cruel. Media can be heartless. Peers can

be brutal. This draws fear that we cannot accomplish anything or that there is a limit to what we are capable of. Each one of us was placed on this earth to achieve BIG THINGS. Each one of us has an eternal power that can only be limited by ourselves, not others. We limit ourselves once we say, "I can't." You can change this by saying, "I CAN," or, "I AM ENOUGH." Do not let others or, more importantly, yourself disown this power, because once you do, you miss the point of why you are great to begin with. You are MORE than good enough!

3. We all feel the need for approval. This is an intriguing subject to tackle because most of us live with others and depend on others throughout our daily routines. For instance, the workplace offers discourse and collaboration. Schools offer professional education and personal growth. Depending on the environment, we need "approval" in order to facilitate progress and logistics. The approvals that we do *not* need are the ones that we believe are necessary to further ourselves. Seeking other's opinions, criticisms, and approval is to only consider other people's perspectives instead of your own. Everyone is responsible for their own happiness and personal growth. It is not your responsibility to make others happy just as they are not responsible for making you happy. Instead, you can consider other's words as "suggestions for improvement" and allow constructive criticism to flourish. You have total free will to interpret and process words to be truths or not, and you have all the capabilities needed to allow those *words* to be your *truth*. Nothing is ever the *truth* unless you *allow* it to be.

4. There is a common phrase that gets shuffled around from person to person: "Well we all make mistakes, *nobody's perfect*." To a certain degree, yes, it is true that we all make mistakes and have missteps. On the other hand, I would argue against the expression *"nobody's*

perfect." Before I address this, let me share with you a realization I had while hiking one day. During one of my weekends, when I was working as a traveling physician at a Native-American reservation in North Las Vegas, I tried to make my way to Red Rock Canyon, one of the national conservation parks in the state of Nevada. The trails there are filled with stunning desert flora and are surrounded by panoramic landscapes of limestone and sandstone that date back to the Triassic period. It was fairly easy to spend a minimum of two hours there and get a good sweat in. The canyon also offered solitude and moments of serenity. During one of my treks, I was staring out into the horizon when a thought suddenly hit me like a ton of bricks.

**Nothing is ever perfect in the eyes of a human.
But in the eyes of the Universe, it already is.**

What this essentially means is that we, as people, tend to focus too much on our shortcomings, frailties, and our imperfections. We tend to focus less on our strengths, talents, and gifts. When we concentrate on our shortcomings, we continue to reinforce how we are not enough or inadequate. Let me invite you to consider another point of view: *if you were not perfect, essentially, you would NOT exist.* Think about this for a moment. Many variables, factors, and perfect timing had to come into play for you to exist in this world. Therefore, you are already *perfect* because you simply exist. You already have everything you need to do great things in this lifetime and in this world. You already come equipped and are ready to go. There is no need to search outside of yourself to fill "voids or gaps." In addition, outside voices can be persuasive and tell you otherwise, but consider this: would you rather spend time concentrating on what others say about you or would you rather rely to your own voice?

*"Don't let the noise of people's opinions
drown out your own inner voice."*

— STEVE JOBS, CO-FOUNDER OF APPLE

Thrive Medicine is not about just pushing forward, but also recognizing that when you do take two steps back in life that there is a lesson to be learned, not judgment or punishment. *Thriving* is about building resilience. Remember that life will always come in *waves*. Surf well. Other's approval can be both overwhelming and convincing, but you get to choose how you want it to dictate your life. Everything and everyone on Earth are already *perfect*. Don't strive for perfection, rather strive for growth, understanding, and compassion. You are more than good enough. You are BRILLIANT!

ACTION STEPS

- Take steps to conquer your fears and misperceptions of yourself. List these steps and create an action plan.

- Surround yourself with people that love and support you.

- Try not to quit on the first try. Keep pushing yourself beyond your comfort zone.

- Find hobbies, work, jobs that keep you mentally challenged and stimulated.

Your thoughts. Your roadmap. Your next steps...

Chapter 10

Fear

"Our deepest fear is not that we are inadequate. Our deepest fear is that we are powerful beyond measure. It is our light, not our darkness, that most frightens us."

— MARIANNE WILLIAMSON

There is a difference between our instinctual fight or flight response and self-preservation biology versus the fear that our minds have created to stop us from fully living our lives. It can limit our human potential. We construct personal roadblocks that automatically stop us from taking the first step. We erect walls to inhibit us from moving forward. How and why does this happen? According to Melanie Greenberg, Ph.D., "Our brains are wired for survival, instead of happiness."[8]

Please take a moment to reflect back on all the times you could not accomplish all the things you wanted because you operated in a state of fear. Missing a sporting event for fear of losing, not showing up for a wedding for fear of doubt, or not singing in your recital for fear of perfectionism. Let's envision this scenario: What if you did not operate in that state of fear? What could you have actually created for yourself instead?

Why is fear an important component of thriving? In some ways, fear is the antithesis of *thriving*. Imagine a flowing river. *Thrive medicine* represents the kinetic energy force to keep moving down the river to wherever it may go. Fear represents the rocks and boulders in the river trying to stop the river's flow. Fear symbolizes the stopgaps in your life, halting and inhibiting you from moving forward. *So, what does water do when it encounters rocks in the middle of the river?* It flows around them. It doesn't crash. *Thrive medicine* is also about creating strategies to *go around* your fears.

Theo Tsaousides, Ph.D., a neuropsychologist, explains how fear can be separated into different categories in our minds:

"Some fears are instinctive…other fears are learned… other fears are taught: cultural norms often dictate whether something should be feared or not.

Fear is also part *imagined*, and so it can arise in the absence of something scary. In fact, because our brains are so efficient, we begin to fear a range of stimuli that are not scary (conditioned fear) or not even present (anticipatory anxiety). We get scared because of what we imagine could happen…But this low-grade, objectless fear can turn into chronic anxiety about nothing specific, and become debilitating."[9]

Let's focus on that last sentence. As a physician, patients come to me for many issues, such as chronic disease management, low back pain, and the common cold. One of the most common issues is chronic anxiety and depression and, from my observations, most of these issues are associated with fear that we have created in our minds—the fear that something may or may not happen. One of the reasons for this is our attachment to the past or the future. For some, the past can influence and sometimes overwhelm their current reality. Some people fear the irrational power that their pasts can take ahold of their lives.

Instead of being skeptical and challenging previous thoughts, they allow the past to run their lives.

Similarly, thoughts of uncertainty and the anticipation of an unknown future disempowers people, unfortunately making them slaves to their thoughts. Sometimes, such debilitating thoughts halt their entire day or, worse, their entire lives. The expression on their faces can range from terror to constant worry. What is it that we are actually afraid of? Even though some fears have labels to them (i.e. rejection, inadequacy, doubt), or even if it is nothing specific at all, they all produce the same outcome: *gripping inhibition.*

During my coaching sessions, one of my clients, Breanne, came to me about something she had been struggling with. She told me that she had been frustrated and sad for some time without being able to pinpoint why. When I asked her what's been going on, she told me, "Well, there is this guy that has been bothering me at work for a while. He changes my desk stationary around, or leaves Post-it notes with messages."

"Sounds like playful flirtation to me," as I observed her tone.

But then she proceeded to tell me that he made a coffee date that he later canceled. Prior to this, they had only been out a couple of times. Breanne was not really ready to try the dating scene since she had just come out of a long-term relationship, but felt very distressed and upset about this particular date cancellation. This caused her several sleepless nights and many disruptions to her work routines. I explained to her that it is less about her questionable relationship with this individual and more about craving to be with someone. Similar to how people have cravings for chocolate, it's less about the chocolate itself and more about how *cravings* and the obsessions/compulsions associated with cravings cause you to stop everything you are doing in order to fulfill a desire. So, the focus is on the *source* of *cravings* and not necessarily what the cravings are for.

In Breanne's particular case, her fear and anxiety was not so much about why this potential date cancelled on her, but more about people of not showing up in her life. This, in turn, reinforced her own independence, which can be viewed as a worthy strength and character trait. However, this resulted in her having fears about trusting others. If you have less trust in others, you develop fewer relationships with people, thus lessening your ability to *thrive* due to lack of connection with others.

In order to *thrive*, we must choose to observe and remain equanimous with our fears. To conquer fear, we need to understand why we have fears in the first place and then address them. The following fears, I believe, are the ones that prevent us from reaching our potential and sharing our gifts with the rest of the world.

» *Fear of being yourself:* Life is sometimes like a theatrical play and, at times, someone else is writing that script. Why would someone else write it though? Is it because you are afraid to step into the limelight of your own stage? Are you letting fear write the script? Let me remind you of something: you are the master of your destiny! You get to choose the script, which characters to include, and the plot. Then, why is it so difficult to just be ourselves? Imagine trying out for a *real* acting audition. Then, right before an audition, your body suddenly stops. Your chatterbox comes on. Your limiting beliefs kick in.

"I will never be good enough."

This type of thought pattern can only control you because it depends on the power of other people's opinions. Other's approval. This can be applied to other scenarios, right? But, guess what? *Who cares what other people think?*

Put the blinders on other people's thoughts and opinions. Do not let it drown out your own inner voice. Let your voice shine through the noise of the outside world. You are the hero of your story. By being yourself, you are sharing yourself and your gifts with the rest of the world. The world needs for you to SHOW UP. Find your gifts now. Practice them day-in and day-out, then showcase them. It is time for you to take the stage.

» *Fear of being happy*: Do not shortchange yourself by not choosing to be happy, because it is, indeed, a choice. Please reread that last sentence. HAPPINESS IS A CHOICE. It does not just happen to you. You can attract happiness by being in the environment that fosters your highest self. For example, choosing friends that support you even when you are not around. Choosing a workplace that promotes your potential. Choosing a significant other that inspires you to do better. Being happy is a process that requires you to practice bringing together all aspects of your life and interconnecting them. It also means not allowing someone or something to take away from who you are. Life is too precious to not be happy. Welcome it now.

» *Fear of success/failure*: We all have dreams. We all have ambitions. We all have aspirations. They are great to write on paper and vision boards, but we also need action to fuel them. Everyone is fully capable of achieving their dreams. So, why do some people accomplish their goals while others do not? It is not dependent on looks, money, or status. It depends on dogged determination and sacrifice. Those who realize their dreams put in the sweat equity it takes, day-in and day-out. However, you will never realize success OR failure if you do not take the first step. Personal success requires you to get up repeatedly after you are knocked down. Criticism and struggle will always be there, like hurdles on a track. Without them, you will not know how high you need to jump or how hard to push yourself. Steven

Spielberg, Oprah, and Steve Jobs are just a few who were told early on to give up. *Well, did they?* The ones who tell you that you can't are usually the ones who have given up themselves. It all comes down to how much you want it and how much you are willing to sacrifice. Forget the fear. Throw it out. Now.

> **One of the vital things to note about fear is this: it is an *illusion*.**
>
> **Let me say that again.**
> **Fear is an illusion, a mirage.**

We have created this illusion which, in turn, stops us in our tracks. Sometimes, we live in this space for so long that it becomes part of our daily lives, habits, and routines. Similar to how fresh cement will eventually harden, having fear as a habit is not something we want set in stone! Theo Tsaousides, Ph.D. also commented that *"fear dictates the actions you take,"* [9] and I have observed many patients and clients alike who have chosen safety and familiarity as their main roads to travel. Now, do not get me wrong, there is nothing wrong about choosing the safer route. But consider this: if you choose the safe route, you allow fear to dictate where you drive, and you don't allow yourself to grow, mature, and learn. We make mistakes for a reason: to learn, not to feel guilt or blame. Allow yourself the opportunity to flourish from being uncomfortable and unfamiliar with the current moment. Learn from it. Stop judging it and yourself.

Also, note that emotions associated with fear are temporary. They are not permanent. There is something comforting in recognizing that negative emotions are short-lived, and that that is already half the battle of freeing yourself from this bind. With the understanding and awareness that fear is temporary, the emotions associated with your fear will have less of a gripping hold on you. The other half is figuring out where your fear stems from. Where are the roots of your fears?

» ***Observe and accept***: Imagine standing outside of a window, peering into the house of your own mind. You notice yourself sitting in the middle of the room. You also observe that the room is filled with your fears, like rejection, work failures, past trauma. In the past, you may have tried to cover up your fears with an external bandage, like alcohol, drugs, or self-abuse. Try to just *observe* and *not react* to the uncomfortable feelings attached to those fears by remembering that you are just looking from the outside in. Observe the feelings course through your body and note them passing through your body. These feelings do not stay with you. Years ago, I learned this meditative technique to hone my body's reactions to outside sensations. In Vipassana meditation, you learn to sit and breathe through these sensations instead of reacting to them.

Another way to look at fear and its associated anxiety is to understand that it gives you an illusion of control.

We do not have control over anything.

I am sure you are thinking of opposable points. What about finances? Marriage? Work? Personal relationships? Well, you may be able to work, but you have no control over the economy or stock market or whether or not you get laid off tomorrow. We have no control over people and what they do or say. Everyone has free choice, whether they believe it or not. We have no control of the weather, and subsequently we have no control over the world outside of us.

The only thing we do have control over is *how we react* to things, people, and events before us, and the choice to be sad, happy, angry, or excited. This very statement makes all the difference and easily shifts how you will view things from now on. It may seem scary to think we have no control over anything, but when we are aware of this very point, then we can *let go* of our attachments and thus the mental strain it takes to "control" everything. Let go of it and you will feel lighter.

What is the worst that can happen?

Have you heard this before? This is such a common expression that we do not stop to actually think twice about. If you apply this question to your fear of *[insert your fear here]*, what is the WORST that COULD happen? *Death* would be the worst case scenario, but guess what? You are still here! Wooooooo!!!!! Hi! How are you? Yes, YOU! You are alive and living proof that your *fear* has not taken over you. Like all things, it takes practice to get out of fear. Some pursue hypnosis, some find cognitive behavioral therapy to be helpful. Nonetheless, it comes down to finding the courage to get out of your fearful state, whether you decide to do it yourself or to seek assistance. Either way, it takes strength and bravery to choose NOT to live a life in fear. It takes repeated tries to step into fear and out of it to appreciate that it is *okay*. You are okay. It is similar to placing your foot in water for the first time. How did you learn that you will not die if you placed your foot in water? Experience maybe? Where did experience come from? Taking the first step, then repeated steps, which then eventually became practice. Where did this practice come from? The *choice* to take a chance.

So, now, would you like to master your fear or let it control you?

In order to *thrive*, one must learn that fear is only as powerful as you allow it to be. Remember that it is also part learned, taught, and imagined. Do not be disillusioned by fear and let it dictate your actions. Observe and do no react to the sensations that come with your fears. *Thrive medicine* is all about flowing around *boulders* in the river of your life. Do not allow fear to prevent you from achieving your highest self!

ACTION STEPS

- Write down your fears and ask where they came from. There is always a source.

- Take little steps outside of your comfort zone each day. Small victories will add up to a large victory.

- Gain support to face your fear. Enlist people that show up for you.

- Relate to those who have the same fear and have already conquered them. What did they do to conquer them?

Your thoughts. Your roadmap. Your next steps...

Chapter 11

Present

"Death is not sad. The sad thing is most people don't live at all."
— Socrates from the movie, *Peaceful Warrior*

Have you ever stopped and smelled the roses? Being in the present moment is quite a challenge in today's age of smartphones, push notifications, YouTube, and Tweets. Seems like everything demands our attention at every second. An essential ingredient of *thriving* is staying with yourself in the moment and being able to utilize all five senses. Here is a snippet from my early school days:

> *6:59am. Oh, no. I am so late.* I hurried and put my clothes on, and rushed out the door. It was a cool, breezy morning. The crispness of the air touched my skin like a warm embrace that I had not felt in a very long time. I was awake as I walked towards the bus. My eyes grew big. Doors opened. I stepped on.
>
> The first day of the fourth grade had finally arrived as I smiled to myself. My family and I had just moved into this new peculiar town. It was our new home. Although I was nervous and anxious as any newcomer

would be, exhilaration also coursed through my veins. Excited to start at a new school, many thoughts crossed my mind.

"Would the new kids like me?"

"Would I make any new friends?"

Crowds of kids swarmed the hallways like worker bees in a hive, just starting the day. Top of the morning, we were all trying to get to our respective homerooms before the bell rang. I looked down at my crumpled paper to look for my homeroom assignment. *Room 17*.

Oh geez, I thought to myself. *I was lucky to find the front door.*

I finally reached my homeroom after asking the hallway monitor. I took a gulp and swallowed.

Here goes nothing...

I turned the doorknob.

I walked silently, but I could still feel heads turn towards my direction. This was my first day, but school actually started two weeks ago. The teacher looked at me and smiled. She motioned me to take a seat.

"Class, please welcome your new classmate."

I quickly took my seat and placed my bag on the floor. I took out my composition book and two mechanical pencils. *Yes, I know. I was a dork back then. I didn't like to sharpen pencils, okay?*

The teacher opened up her book and placed her eyeglasses on. She had a lovely charm about her. She was wearing a freshly pressed magenta dress top, and her hair was tucked back in a bun. Her rosy cheeks welcomed us. I immediately felt at ease as if I had been in this new school for the past six months. The teacher fingered down a list.

"Okay, class, I am going to take attendance. Please raise your hand when I call your name."

Oh, boy, I thought to myself. Beads of sweat rolled down my forehead.

"Ashley?

Scott?

Jason?"

Man, I did not like the feeling of attention on me. I had gotten into a couple of schoolyard fights at my last school and into a lot of trouble, not only by receiving detentions, but with my parents as well. They were not pleased with me. I did not like the looks I received back then—the looks of disgust and disappointment from my last teacher and classmates. I beat myself up to do better. *Isn't it funny that we grow up to do the same thing as adults?*

I wanted to start fresh, to start over again in this new place.

"Julie?

Justine?

Colin...Zhuu-u?"

My racing thoughts suddenly halted at that moment. Everything silenced. My focus sharpened towards the teacher, everything zoomed in. I quickly stood up out of my seat and raised my hand high.

"I'M HERE!!! I'M HERE. PRESENT!" I yelped.

A couple of the girls next to me giggled to themselves. The teacher smiled and encouraged me to sit down. I felt a wave of embarrassment across my face as it flushed bright red.

Who jumps up out of their seat during roll call?

All eyes were on the new boy, only this time, I smirked in return. Something was different. I decided to stay out of the past and focus on the current moment. What was the point of referring to the past when I realized that I was already missing my current reality? The fourth grade was going to pass me by if I did not pay attention to my reality.

There are two points to this story: *letting go of the past and being mindful in the current moment.*

There is no need to wonder what once was. Those moments are gone. The past serves as a reminder that the events we have lived out just simply happened. There is no need to harbor judgment about them. The past does not define who we are. Many people victimize themselves by letting the past take over, by overwhelming their world. For example, you may think that you are a "bad" daughter because you neglected to do as you were told by your father. You may also think that you are not the brightest student because you ranked third in your class. These and many other examples are simply events that JUST occurred. They are there to remind you that you get to make a different choice when a similar event arrives again. This concept can also be applied to future-thinking as well. Do not allow the past and future take us away from the present—*this very moment.*

Furthermore, I've noticed over the years that my memories have the strongest impact and are the most memorable when I choose to be present. Another way to put this is that the more I use my senses and am mindful in the current moment, the more ever-lasting my memory remains in my latter years. So, for example, with this above story, I remember the scent of fresh lead from all the mechanical pencils I had to the screeching sounds the chalk made when my teacher wrote her name on the board. Being present is a powerful tool in *Thrive Medicine* because the more we are present with ourselves, the more life we are able to live and enjoy.

In our current world of advanced technology and social media, pedestrians cross streets while looking down at their phones and walking past each other. There are also buses full of passengers who do not look at each other. In this world, we eat, talk, text, and watch the news simultaneously. In this world, we step over each other by not listening and just wanting to get our point in to win an argument. In this world, the only time we are not bombarded with paid advertising is when we go to sleep.

Let me ask you:

> **Do you remember what you ate for lunch yesterday?**
>
> **Do you remember the last conversation you had with your folks?**
>
> **When was the last time you gazed at the stars?**

Quite simply, we live in a world full of distractions, whether it is from constant phone calls, being stuck in gridlock traffic with radios blasting, or our smartphones going off every five seconds. It is quite noisy! Our world is full of noise, smoke, and distractions—things that constantly take us away from the only thing that matters:

THIS MOMENT.

What do I mean by this? Let me break it down. This moment means this very second—this very instance in which you are holding this book and reading these very words, the current moment now that you just took a breath and sipped your water or coffee.

Let's try this exercise:

Turn off your phone and tell your present company you will be gone for the next five minutes. Don't worry, I'll bring you back.

Look for a flower outside, either in a nearby garden or park. Go to the next flower that catches your attention. Okay, look at each petal. What color is it? Look at the contours of each petal. Is one of them broken? Do you see any critters on it? What are they doing? Now, lean close, shut your eyes, and smell the flower. What does it smell like? Take three sniffs. Does it smell sweet? Like dirt? Fresh? *Excellent.* Now, cradle the flower in your hands. Careful, you are a giant compared to the flower. Close your eyes. What does it feel like? Firm? Soft? Fragile? Take ten seconds doing this. Next, reach down to the stem (caution if there are thorns)! Feel the support of the stem holding the flower up. It feels strong and tall, right? *Amazing, I know.*

If there aren't any flowers nearby, reach for your coffee or tea cup. Close your eyes. What do you feel? Warmth... your cup embraced by your hands. What else? Is it a paper cup? Styrofoam? Ceramic mug? Next, take a whiff. What is that aroma? Is it a mocha, whipped, or a pumpkin-spiced frappuccino? Or is it a serene chamomile tea?

This exercise can be applied to anything. All it requires is that you focus your attention on one thing AND one thing at a time. Yes, it may seem simple, but actually it is much more difficult if you are out of practice.

Where was your mind at when you were doing this? Were you truly focused on the flower or the cup of tea? Or did your mind fill up with thoughts like, "What am I going to make for dinner?" or, "Who is going to pick up the kids from baseball practice?" or, "Did I walk the dog this morning?" It's okay if you did. If your mind didn't wander and you were able to follow along, then KUDOS to you! You were able to block out distractions from your mind at THAT moment and *be present and focused.* Even if you did, do not be surprised if your thoughts came pouring back in right after the exercise. It takes practice. Daily practice. A lifetime of practice.

So, the next question is, why is *this moment* the only thing that matters? Well, let's look at the big picture:

Life is a series of moments—notable moments and sometimes moments forgotten. It is your choice whether to make those moments worth remembering—moments that make your hair stand up, moments where you could not stop laughing, you fell over, moments where you looked into the eyes of your beloved and the world stopped. In the present moment, you can simply enjoy everything around you because you chose to focus, pay attention, and be present to the realization that life is ALL around you. Whether you are alone in your room reading this, in a busy cafe, or on a bustling bus, life is happening around you all the time, whether you choose to be present or not. So, BE present, BE here, because once the moment passes, it is gone. You can never get it back.

~ ~ ~

The present is a *gift*...

> *"Yesterday is history.*
> *Tomorrow is a mystery.*
> *Today is a gift.*
> *That's why it's called the present."*
> — ALICE MORSE EARLE

My nostalgic childhood memory from above also highlights another crucial point. The present is also a chance to start over anew. Consider this: when you wake up in the morning, have you ever reflected on the fact that you actually woke up *alive*? If never given a chance to wake up again, would you have had any regrets from the life you lived thus far? Using a previous *Thrive Medicine* strategy, gratitude allows us to reflect on how lucky we are to live the life we have lived. Never mind if you have regrets or have made mistakes in the past. We all have. The current moment, the present, today is your second chance to press the *refresh* button. That is such a gift! It is a miracle that you are given a second chance in life because you woke up this morning. It gives you the opportunity to choose differently— choices to lead your life either the same way or to veer off the beaten path and to create your own brand-new trail. Getting into the practice of viewing today as a gift will set yourself up for the better in the long haul because you essentially shift how you perceive and live your life. That is *thriving*, choosing better.

Your life is a gift. Do not waste it. Your life is a canvas. Paint it and create your masterpiece.

Hone your senses to be more mindful in your current surroundings. Remember that your past and future do not define you. You get to redefine yourself every single day. Your life shifts for the better when you treat today as a gift.

ACTION STEPS

- Read *Way of The Peaceful Warrior* (by Dan Millman), or if time-pressed watch the movie *Peaceful Warrior*.

- We live in a highly visually stimulating world. Let us try using our other senses. The supermarket is my one of favorite places to train them. Head over to the produce aisle and give it a try. You'll gain a whole new perspective.

- Make a list of other places where you can do this. Schedule a time when you can go train your senses.

- Nature is a fantastic training ground in which to be mindful. Leave all technology behind and let Mother Nature envelop you.

Your thoughts. Your roadmap. Your next steps...

_____

_____

_____

_____

_____

_____

_____

_____

_____

_____

_____

_____

_____

_____

_____

_____

_____

Chapter 12

The Choice

*"In the end, it is important to remember
that we cannot become what we need to be
by remaining what we are."*
— Max De Pree

Now that you have arrived at the end of the book, you've now figured out that you can leave an indelible mark on the world. Now you understand that your decisions influence those around you. Yes, you are THAT powerful. Whether you choose to run and hide or stand up and trudge forward, it is your choice. This last chapter serves to summarize and reinforce all the components of *thriving. Let's get right to it.*

When the concept of *Thrive Medicine* came into fruition, it came down to one solitary word: *choice.* This very word opened up a whole new world for me. It allows me to fully express who I am each and every day.

Five years ago, I awoke from my slumber. Out of all my life experiences, this wake-up call was the most significant—it was a type of awakening that suggested I could no longer continue living life so aimlessly and routinely after realizing the truth. The truth I found is that every human has the potential and opportunity to do amazing things on this beautiful planet with their limited amount of time, not just to simply pass time. I no longer wanted to take things and people for granted, and I asked myself, *If today was my last day on Earth, would I be satisfied with everything so far?*

When I understood this *truth*, I took it upon myself to make different choices in my life; choices that led to another event, another moment, or another opportunity—ones that built upon each other, like railroad tracks connecting one end to another. With one of my greatest choices, I was able to get out of my depression by leaving my environment while also staying in the medical profession. This one choice eventually led me to lead culinary workshops, teaching physicians how to cook as a survival skill in order to combat our current obesity epidemic. I have also been afforded the unique opportunity to travel all over the world in addition to doctoring in various states in America.

Please, don't get me wrong. Not all my choices have led to "great" outcomes. I also had many failures and self-defeats. My missteps demonstrated to me that we can all learn, grow, and mature from our experiences if we choose to. My lesson is that you cannot have success without failure, you cannot have love without heartbreak, and you cannot *thrive* without *conscious choices*.

Before my awakening, I neither understood this concept nor recognized who I was. Sometimes, one can certainly go through life without a direction or a roadmap. *So, what ends up happening?* You inevitably get lost and, at times, confused.

This awakening occurred after I graduated from medical school and I was transitioning to the next chapter of my life, which was medical residency. However, unlike my other fellow classmates, there was a nine-month break until my next chapter.

What do I do for nine months?

Up until that point, I had spent over a third of my life studying to become a physician. I did not know how to NOT do anything. I was very acquainted with *being busy* and basically nothing else. *This is pathetic,* I thought to myself. For some of my colleagues, some would have gone on doing research, while others would have worked in a healthcare-type job to build up their resume. At that point, I didn't understand the concept of *"to be"* versus *"to do."* In other words, I didn't know how to be mindful.

I was at a low.

You might ask, "Why??? You just completed medical school and were on your way to residency, and you basically had nine months off! Go relax!" This was certainly not the case with me. I did not have that specific drive to just have fun yet. There was something amiss, something that was empty inside of me. I recalled a conversation between me and my little sister:

"What's wrong, brother?" she asked with her left eyebrow raised. Despite our childhood rowdiness, our bond was rooted and became more tethered over the years.

"I'm not sure. I'm a little tired and mentally fatigued. I just don't know what to do next with these upcoming months," I mentioned, letting out a deep sigh.

"How about doing... *nothing?*" she replied. I raised my eyebrow in return.

"What do you mean?" I asked inquisitively.

"Exactly that. *Nothing,*" she replied with her trademark smug tone.

Later that evening, she wrote me a letter, which she rarely does.

"Hi, brother. Just wanted to let you know how loved you are and that I am excited and so grateful that we have each other on this journey to change the world. Trust the process and the journey. I think being with yourself is the greatest test to measure your own self-love.

Sitting still and being with just you will be a skill that will bring you more harmony and peace in your life despite all your accomplishments. If you can accomplish so much yet have a problem sitting with yourself then you may be lacking inner peace. When you define yourself by the people you love and the things you have done, regardless of external things, who are you? That is for you to answer.

These are all a part of you, but you need to be able to cultivate the love that is separate from another person. Then you will find peace wherever you are."

That following year, I stepped into my own shoes for the first time.

In all honesty, how you want to define your life comes down to what you want to contribute to the world. And are you willing to do what it takes to achieve it? What will be your legacy? What will you leave behind that you want others to remember you by?

Let's try this exercise:

Imagine your unexpected funeral procession. The six o'clock news reported there was a terrible motor vehicle accident on the freeway last week. Your family and close friends are there, surrounding your casket. Autumn leaves have fallen onto a blanket of rustic gold and brown petals. Many of them are weeping, others are holding hands. Your best friend walks up to the podium and starts your eulogy.

What will they say about you? How would you like to be remembered? What will you leave behind for others? Please take a pause and think about this because, in a way, this prioritizes the essentials of your life. Perhaps your relationships and ties with loved ones instead of the accumulation of money and things are what is important. To reiterate from a previous chapter, we cannot take anything with us when we pass on, so why not cultivate everlasting memories and experiences instead? *Thriving* is all about leaving your mark on the earth. It is about constantly striving to make an impact not just on yourself, but on others as well.

"How will you serve the world? What do they need that your talent can provide? I can tell you from experience that the effect you have on others is the most valuable currency there is."
— JIM CARREY

Choose things that empower you.

Let's get real. Why choose things that repudiate who you are? You pick a job just to pay the bills, but you absolutely hate it. Then why do you do it? Not only will you become more frustrated and angry over time, but you waste valuable time as well! I appreciate the need to pay the electric bill, but there are other ways to go about it. Beef up your resume, pursue higher education, reinforce your talents and skills. Go and express things that empower you!

Choose something that propels you toward an inspiring future.

Time is the only precious commodity that we cannot renew. We can always acquire more money, clothes, cars, and even friends. However, in order to *thrive*, put yourself in a direction that leads to a better future, whether it is a new job that can be expanded or a partner that will inspire you and help you grow. Or travel to a place outside of your boundaries that will take you to new personal heights. Try a new language. If you want to learn Bulgarian, for example, but do not plan on visiting the country or have anyone to converse with then what would be the point of learning it? Learning a new language might open new business opportunities or perhaps new dating opportunities might manifest because you decided to bridge a gap with another person.

Surround yourself with supportive people that promote a higher version of yourself.

Whenever I counsel patients about smoking cessation or improving their nutrition and lifestyle, I usually get the same stories or excuses:

"Doctor, it's hard for me to stop smoking when my wife still smokes at home."

"Doc, whenever I try to eat better, I get these different looks from my family and friends at the dinner table."

"None of my friends want to come to the gym with me."

Most of the time, besides personal motivation, your environment is one of the hardest things to change. When one finally decides to quit smoking and they have every ounce of the drive needed to change their habits, they encounter a roadblock that they did not anticipate. Finding the personal drive to change is difficult enough, but when you are excited to share your changes with your family members or close friends, this is where many people find resistance and where most falter. This can be applied to many things, including finding a new job or changing your romantic partner or considering living in a new city. When you do not have support, it can be very challenging. Having an encouraging environment is similar to having someone push you up over a high physical wall. Just that little push will help you overcome something that may seem insurmountable. Suggestions would be to make new friends, visit a different coffee shop, move to another city, or end a negative relationship. You know you are in a supportive environment when the steps to change your habits (smoking, diet, etc.) are made *easier* for you to implement by the people around you, not harder.

Treat negative events as opportunities to discover and grow.

Let's face it. We may not have the good fortune of having the best people in our lives or being able to live in the safest cities or having the best childhood or being financially sound from the beginning. We may not get the jobs that we want or attract the kindest romantic partners. We may even face death once or, for some, several times. Others may face heartbreak and even fall into depression. Each one of these examples presents a new *choice* for us—whether to suffer or to learn, grow, and mature. I suggest the latter. Do not be the victim of your story. Be the hero that inspires others to rise up.

Get ready to jump.

Like all big decisions you have made in your life, you have to be ready to make them. Be conscious of where you are in your life and decide whether you are ready to make that leap. Choose whether something or someone is good for you or not. This is not an over exaggeration, but your life does depend on this because your future is dictated by the decisions you make today. There is no problem with taking risks, but take them consciously.

Recall the last time you got to make your OWN decision. Think hard about this. The last time you went on a vacation, bought a piece of clothing, adopted a pet, left a romantic partner, changed jobs, or simply chose a restaurant. Was it your decision or was it influenced by someone else? If it was not your decision but you allowed it, how did it feel to you? Did it feel like you lost power or control over your thoughts or choices? Now, I understand if you asked for a suggestion or an opinion. However, making a decision without considering your own input or voice can render you powerless, and can sometimes be paralyzing. It does not have to be that way. You can choose differently. Own your power. Stand firm and rooted. Choose yourself. Go and create that solid foundation. There is only upwards and forwards.

As you are about to come to a close, place the book down and move on with your life, just remember that *today* is a choice in which you can decide to do something different. *Thrive medicine* is a concept that was born out of realizing that it was imperative to change the status quo of my life. Waking up to this realization meant I had to make decisions more consciously, not just to prevent previous mistakes, but to push myself further. As you reflect on this, know that you are the sum of all your choices up until this current moment. The next step is figuring out how your upcoming choices will affect your present and future, and which direction you want to take in your life.

» Immerse yourself in a fostering environment that supports the true you.

» Treat every negative event as a mile marker to grow from.

» Make a conscious decision about who/what gets to enter your life.

Are you satisfied with the *default life* or do you want more and to *thrive?!* That is power of choice!

**It is time to elevate to your best life.
Your life starts right NOW!**

*"Set a goal to achieve something that is
so big, so exhilarating that it excites you and
scares you at the same time. It must be a
goal that is so appealing, so much in line with
your spiritual core, that you can't get it out of
your mind. If you do not get chills
when you set a goal, you're not setting
big enough goals."*
— STEVEN LIN, 3X NATIONAL TAEKWONDO CHAMPION

ACTION STEPS

- Make a list of brand new choices for yourself. Examples: pursuing a new passion, planning a once forgotten trip, meeting a new person, or applying for a job that you always wanted.

- Make a list of steps to reach each choice. Break it down. This makes it more manageable and feasible.

- Create a vision board of what your ideal life would look like in one, three, or five years from now. No inhibitions. Nothing is stopping you.

- Create a similar vision board for your ideal partner, family relationship, ideal career, etc.

- Then write over each vision board, "I CHOOSE MYSELF!"

Your thoughts. Your roadmap. Your next steps...

Acknowledgements

Mom and Dad - Thank you for all the sacrifices that you both have made for me and Donnie to be able to live a solid life after you immigrated to America. I know there were trying and challenging times, so we both really appreciate it immensely. Thank you for your assertiveness, gentleness, love, and understanding for all my passions, dreams, and sometimes crazy ventures!

Sister - No words can describe how lucky I am to have you as a sibling in this lifetime. It brings me to tears every time I think about that first home video of you throwing eggs at me, and when you were a toddler playing in our makeshift "kitchen" of Play-Doh. I am grateful and blessed to spend this lifetime with you.

Nino, Jimmy, and Rex - No guy can ask for a better circle of best friends than you three. We have traveled the world together, and have been through the ups and downs of each other's lives. I am eternally grateful to have you three for your counsel and support.

Mentors - There are too many to count. To all my family medicine mentors, life mentors, and coaches, who've all became genuine friends, thank you for your sincerity and support over the years. You all have contributed to the person I am today. I am truly humbled.

Dear friends - Thank you for your deep and insightful conversations that have literally slowed down time for me because it gave me pause on what was truly important. Some of you, I met only once, and some are still with me, but I will always carry an essence of each of you with me wherever I go.

To my grandfathers - One whom I never had the chance to meet and the other who I met, but has passed on. My maternal grandfather was an author and my paternal grandfather was a doctor. Never in my wildest dreams would I have imagined that I later in my life, would have combined the two paths. It is very surreal and amazing to think about it. Thank you, both for paving those roads for me.

References

INTRODUCTION:
[1]"What is Lifestyle Medicine?" *American College of Lifestyle Medicine.*

CHAPTER 1: LIFE:
[2]National Center for Health Statistics. "Life Expectancy." *Centers for Disease Control and Prevention.*

CHAPTER 2: DOING:
[3]Nevison, Oak Associates. "Productive vs. actual work hours, from a collection of four studies." *CIRCADIAN FRMS and 24/7 Workforce Solutions.*

[4]Caruso, C., Ph.D., R.N., Hitchcock, E., et al. "Overtime and Extended Work Shifts: Recent Findings on Illnesses, Injuries, and Health Behaviors." *U.S. Department of Health and Human Services, Centers for Disease Control and Prevention, National Institute for Occupational Safety and Health,* 2004.

CHAPTER 3 WANDERLUST:
[5]Ray, R., Sanes, M., & Schmitt, J. "No-Vacation Nation Revisited." *Center for Economic and Policy Research,* 2013.

[6]Hess, A. "On holiday: Countries with the most vacation days." *USA TODAY,* 2013.

CHAPTER 8: AUTHENTICITY:

[7]Andrew, L., MD, JD. "Physician Suicide." *Medscape*, 2017.

CHAPTER 10: FEAR:

[8]Greenberg, M., Ph.D. "Why We Can't Just Get Rid of Anxiety & Distress." *Psychology Today*, 2013.

[9]Tsaousides, T., Ph.D. "7 Things You Need to Know About Fear." *Psychology Today*, 2015.

About the Author

 Colin, first and foremost, is a student of *life*, always willing to learn and take on more. Colin takes in all the life experiences he can possibly muster for his personal and professional growth, and to share with his audiences.

Colin has studied osteopathic medicine in West Virginia and is board-certified in Family Practice and Osteopathic Manipulative Treatment. Also, he is amongst the first class of physicians in the world to be board-certified in Lifestyle Medicine. In addition, he studied health-supportive and plant-based culinary arts at the Natural Gourmet Institute and health coaching at the Institute for Integrative Nutrition, both of which are located in Manhattan, New York.

He enjoys globetrotting, triathlon racing, bachata dancing, and coffee in his personal time. He personally *thrives* on connecting with all walks of life. He currently lives in Los Angeles, California.

Made in the USA
Middletown, DE
11 July 2019